NEW TYPES OF
OLD AMERICANS AT HARVARD

LONDON : HUMPHREY MILFORD

OXFORD UNIVERSITY PRESS

NEW TYPES OF
OLD AMERICANS AT HARVARD

AND AT EASTERN WOMEN'S COLLEGES

BY

GORDON TOWNSEND BOWLES

Cambridge, Massachusetts

HARVARD UNIVERSITY PRESS

1932

PRINTED AT THE HARVARD UNIVERSITY PRESS

CAMBRIDGE, MASS., U.S.A.

Foreword

GENETICS AND ANTHROPOLOGY are such comparatively recent sciences that precise observations of families extending over more than two generations are extremely rare. Harvard University is sufficiently old so that membership in it has become traditional for many sons of New England families. Dr. William T. Brigham and Dr. Dudley A. Sargent, early directors of the Hemenway Gymnasium, were so enlightened as to record and file the physical measurements of Harvard men from the late sixties on. Hence there has existed for many years, in dead storage, an invaluable mass of data on the bodily characteristics of Harvard sons, fathers, and grandfathers, which is virtually unique. The analysis of such material should afford a brief glimpse of the most recent phases of physical evolution in males of Old American stock.

Consequently, when Dr. John C. Phillips intimated his willingness to finance a study of the growth changes in young Americans, a long-awaited opportunity had arrived and was seized firmly by the forelock. I selected for this important investigation Mr. Gordon Townsend Bowles, a very promising graduate student in Physical Anthropology. This young scientist has shown the most remarkable industry and initiative in carrying his task to a satisfactory conclusion. Not content with the records of Harvard men alone, he has secured and analyzed comparative data relating to similar physical changes in mothers and daughters who have attended Vassar, Wellesley, Smith, and Mount Holyoke colleges. I do not think that I exaggerate when I describe the work of Mr. Bowles as one of the most significant contributions to our knowledge of recent human evolution. Many papers have been written demonstrating apparent increases of stature and weight in different college generations of unrelated groups of individuals. So far as I am aware, the present work is the first effort to study these phenomena in grandfathers, fathers, and sons, and in mothers and daughters, on the basis of their measurements at corresponding ages (during the period of their college attendance).

I have no intention of offering here a premature disclosure of Mr. Bowles' results. Writers of forewords, like readers of detective stories, should not tell.

This volume has suffered the disadvantage of being issued during Mr. Bowles' sojourn in China as a Harvard-Yenching Research Fellow. Consequently he has been unable to read the proof. Editorial liberties, however, have not been allowed to degenerate into license. Mrs. Pearl B. Hurwitz has exercised great skill and forbearance in this task.

The expenses of the investigation were generously defrayed by Dr. John C. Phillips, and the editorial work was completed with the help of a gift by Mr. James H. Proctor.

EARNEST A. HOOTON

HARVARD UNIVERSITY
Cambridge, Massachusetts
July 1, 1932

Acknowledgments

AT THE outset it must be stated that, were due credit given to the many people through whose interest and coöperation alone this study has been made possible, the list of acknowldgements would run into several pages. Mention must be made, however, of those who have been of especial help through the furnishing of material or valuable suggestions.

Special thanks are due to Mr. D. W. Bailey and the members of the staff of the Alumni Directory of Harvard University for access to the numerous files and class records, and for information concerning families and alumni, and to Miss Martha Seltzer of Radcliffe College, who is responsible for the larger share of the statistical work. Thanks are due also to Mr. C. B. Van Wyck of the Physical Education Department of Harvard College and the Hemenway Gymnasium for the use of records taken under the supervision of Dr. D. A. Sargent and for unpublished statistical data; to Dr. Ruth Elliott and Miss Jane Couch of the Mary Hemenway Gymnasium, Wellesley College, for data from Wellesley; to Miss Ruth MacDuffie of the Biology Department of Vassar College for material from Vassar; and to the Departments of Physical Education of Smith and Mt. Holyoke Colleges for series from their respective institutions. To the War Department at Washington I am indebted for information regarding soldiers of the Revolutionary War; to Mr. Lawrence Jenkins of the Peabody Museum, Salem, Massachusetts, for measurements on sailors of the Peabody Ships; and to the numerous alumni of Harvard College for their generous replies to letters of inquiry.

Finally, I am extremely grateful to Dr. E. A. Hooton of the Division of Anthropology of Harvard University for numerous suggestions as regards both material and treatment. To his constant interest in the progress of the work and his encouragement and generous coöperation in its completion are due the results of this study, which it is hoped will contribute somewhat to the large but as yet little explored field of local anthropology, the interests of which are not realized until objectively surveyed.

Contents

Tables in the Text

List of Figures

EXPLANATIONS AND ABBREVIATIONS

IN A normal sample of any given number of measurements there is a range represented by two extremes. Between these extremes, the smallest and the greatest, lie all of the other figures. These tend to produce, when graphically tabulated, a frequency distribution which, if the conditions were perfect, would form according to the laws of chance a bell-shaped curve (normal probability curve), the bulk of the figures falling in the middle and the remainder tapering off at both ends.

By experiment it has been established that in a normal or perfect distribution there is a certain definite ratio of deviation from the mean towards both ends of the curve. Since in casual samplings of small numbers, such as those of the present study, the conditions will not produce normal frequency curves, it is necessary to calculate certain quantities called statistical constants which will explain the extent of variability of the frequencies from the arithmetical mean and will give some criterion for determining the values of the series. The statistical constants used in this study are as follows:

No. ...... Number or frequencies of observations or individuals.

M .... Arithmetical mean of a series.

σ .... Standard deviation. This is a quantity which varies with the dispersion of each group and represents the root-mean-square deviation from the mean. Its value lies in determining the general dispersion from the mean, and is for convenience expressed algebraically in its root-mean-square form. It expresses the extent to which the average individual in a series may be expected to deviate from the mean of the entire series.

v .... The coefficient of variation. This is the standard deviation expressed as a percentage of the mean in order to have a basis of comparison between series of measurements of different magnitudes.

r .... The coefficient of correlation. This indicates the degree of relationship existing between two given series of measurements in terms of unity. Thus, since sons are taller than their fathers it is expected that they will also be heavier. As observed in the text (pp. 54 ff.) this is the case, and there is therefore a positive correlation. In case these sons were lighter there would be a certain degree of negative correlation.

p.e. ...... The probable error (preceded by the sign $\pm$). In any sample, the arithmetical mean is likely to be unrepresentative because of the unevenness of the distribution. Assuming the distribution to be normal, the probable error represents such a quantity within a range of which, on either side of the mean, the chances are even that the true arithmetical mean of an indefinitely large sample will fall. In short, it represents the margin of error that must be ascribed to the mean of any sample. The probable errors of σ and v are similar quantities which to a certain extent give an idea of the reliability of these constants.

Other Abbreviations

C .... Coefficient of mean square contingency. This is merely a convenient means of determining the relationship between two observed traits such as pigmentation of the skin and eyes or of the same trait in two different groups. Since perfect association is unity, a coefficient of .30 (p. 61) indicates that the degree of association or similarity between the two given groups is only 30 per cent, or about one-third perfect. Usually resemblances between parents and children for any given trait are in the neighborhood of .50, or one-half perfect.

Σ .... Sum of (p. 76).

Ma and Mb   The means of two groups or individuals designated a and b (p. 76).

N and F ..   Normal and full (expanded) chest measurements (Tables 45, 48, etc.).

Weights are always given in pounds and measurements, except where otherwise indicated, in centimeters (1 centimeter = .394 in.). The correlation tables are always arranged with the older individuals (fathers, mothers, older brothers, and older sisters) on the vertical columns of measurement intervals, and the younger individuals on the horizontal (p. 54, footnote). This means that the more or less vertical and horizontal zigzag lines are formed by the joining of the means of the different arrays (columns) of the fathers and sons respectively.

The statistical methods employed in the present study are used by all students of biometrics, and have been devised for the most part by Karl Pearson and his school. They are described at length in any standard work on statistics such as that of Yule.

NEW TYPES OF
OLD AMERICANS AT HARVARD

Chapter I

PURPOSE AND MATERIAL

THE original purpose of this investigation was to determine the changes in physical measurements and proportions in the families of Old Americans. The first task was to gather together and arrange all data from readily accessible sources yielding the largest number of measurements with which comparisons could be made. When this had been completed the work resolved itself into a more comprehensive, three-fold problem: firstly, to determine the change in Old Americans, if any, by generations; secondly, to determine the increase by periods considering all individuals as belonging to one class, i. e. making no distinction as to generation; thirdly, to determine if precedence in age among brothers or sisters has any influence on bodily proportions and measurements.

Sufficient material has already been made available through measurements on army and navy recruits, prisoners, hospital patients, inmates of asylums, and through other institutional records, to obtain a fairly accurate idea of the physique of the general population in New England. It is a matter of regret, however, that only army and navy and other student records are comparable with the present study which is based largely on students, since, in the case of the other sources mentioned, age, general physical condition, and other factors combine to lessen their comparative value. No attempt has been made to collect and analyze already existing data, but rather to furnish new statistical facts, and more especially on the rather highly selected group of students from Harvard and various women's colleges.

A further source of material, and one which proved far more profitable than at first anticipated, was the records of soldiers of New Hampshire in the Revolutionary War, and sailors of the Peabody Ships of Salem, Massachusetts, during the period of mercantile expansion immediately prior to the War of 1812.

The soldiers may be considered as a fair random sample of the population, covering a range in age from 15 to 50 and not subject to the selective limitations of the student groups. The sailors, on the

other hand, seem to be a more or less selected lot. In point of time
they succeed the soldiers by a generation, but are slightly smaller.
It seems likely, however, that the ships' masters chose the shorter
men because they were steadier on their feet, took up less room, and
ate less food. Whatever the economical motives be, sea folk are
often shorter than their inland neighbors in areas where such comparisons can be made. These earlier records are utilized only for
general comparison with the student material which forms the main
body of data. It was because of the lack of any early material that
it seemed advisable to include the two groups under discussion.

The term "Old American," as defined by Hrdlička,[1] includes all
whose ancestors are of American parentage for at least two generations. In the present study it is used in the same meaning for the
younger generations (i. e. fathers and more especially sons), but is
employed rather reservedly with reference to the next ascending
generation, inasmuch as usually parentage alone and not grand-
parentage is indicated.

In the case of the soldiers of the Revolutionary War and the
Peabody Ships' Seamen the contributory racial elements are far
more questionable than for the students for whom there exist quite
adequate information which lends itself to classification, not only of
racial, but also of occupational factors.

As seen in Table 1, the proportion of extra-nationals to Old
Americans among the sons is slightly less than 6 percent. Of this
number 4 percent are British and only 2 percent Continental or
mixed. Of the Continentals again, all but .24 percent are either
German or mixed British and Continental. The proportion is so
insignificant as to be negligible. The occurrence of extra-nationals
is due to the fact that in many cases a grandparent, in a few cases
a parent, was of foreign descent. The percentages represent the
totals of these minor groups which are present in different degrees
in different individuals. In the case of the fathers the extra-nationality is slightly higher but does not exceed 10 percent of the entire
series. In some cases also, it must be noted, extra-nationality in the
sons is from the maternal rather than the paternal side. It must also
be remembered that the indication of American as one's race is not
a safe criterion. At best we can but assume that in all probability
the material for the students at least is largely American, and that

---

[1] A. Hrdlička, *Old Americans* (1925), pp. 4–5.

any foreign blood that may be represented is almost entirely from sources which originally contributed to the ancestry of the larger parent stock.

TABLE 1

PERCENTS OF EXTRA-NATIONALITY OF SONS

		British				British and Continental	Continental		Total
English	Scotch	Irish	Welsh	Canadian	Mixed	Mixed	German	Others	European
1.58	.53	.53	.06	.38	.83	.82	.82	.24	....
Totals		3.91				.82	1.06		5.79

EXTRA-NATIONALS IN PROPORTION TO OLD AMERICANS

European 5.79

Old American 94.21

Total 100.00

On the whole, then, we may conclude that practically all of the students included in this study are of two or three generation English, Scotch, Irish, and German ancestry. Wherever there was any doubt, either on account of name or designated nationality, the individual or pair was rejected. It is probably safe to assume that 80 to 90 percent of the peoples included in the student groups are of Old American stock. Except for comparative data, the sources of material for measurements on the males were limited exclusively to Harvard University.

Through the courtesy of the Department of Physical Education the series of 18,000 measurements made by, or under the supervision of, Dr. Sargent at the Hemenway Gymnasium were secured. The material covered measurements made between the years 1880 and 1917 (the entrance of the United States into the World War). In order to make use of these cards, which included over 40 measurements, it was first necessary to secure genealogies of all men who went to Harvard before 1917 whose fathers were also Harvard students after the year 1880. All of the class records and necrology files at the Alumni Records office were gone over carefully and a total of over 2000 couples was secured (95 percent from the College, the Lawrence Scientific School, and the Law School, and the remainder from the Medical School). Unfortunately the Sargent cards recorded only about one-third of the student body. In many cases, therefore, where the father's card was present the son's was lacking, and vice versa. The net result yielded 421 pairs, of which cards were available for both fathers and sons.

Between the years 1870 and 1880, Dr. William T. Brigham, formerly college physician, took measurements of about 2000 students. His measurements were essentially the same as those on the Sargent cards, and it was possible, by using the Sargent cards for the sons, to obtain an additional 60 couples, making a total of 481 couples. Of these, however, several duplicated the fathers (i. e. brothers having the same father), and the net result yielded 400 fathers and 481 sons, a total of 881 individuals. Not all of the cards are complete, but in all except one instance the most vital measurements — height and weight — are given. After the year 1917 the College required medical examinations and the Sargent series was discontinued. The medical examination blanks on file at Wadsworth House were gone over, and by again consulting the Alumni Records office nearly 1600 couples out of a possible 4000 were secured by using the Sargent cards and Brigham Register records for the fathers and the medical sheets for the sons.

Figure 1 shows the number of couples used in the present study in proportion to the increase of second generation Harvard men and the total number of students enrolled. The heavy line represents the total number of men enrolled each year in the College,[1] the broken line the number of second generation men, and the stippled line the number of couples utilized in the present survey. It will be noticed that the total enrollment has grown considerably more proportionally than the number of second generation men. This is probably due more to the rapid increase, especially since the war, than to any actual falling off in attendance on the part of the sons of Harvard men. The years indicated on the horizontal plane are class years; consequently the period of America's entry into the World War dates from 1921, and the period of depression lasts roughly until 1924.

The data for the third and fourth ascending generations were secured by sending letters of inquiry to the fathers of the small series (400). The letter stated the purpose for which information was being

---

[1] The figures were obtained from the first annual reports of the different classes. The numbers are somewhat variable, on account of different standards of selecting class members. In some instances transfer students, associate members, and honorary members are included, in others they are omitted. The variations are not, however, significant.

gathered and included a blank to be filled out and returned. To the 300 odd letters sent to the living parents approximately 250 replies were received. In many cases, however, the individual was uncertain in regard to his father or gave an approximate figure the value

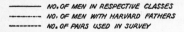

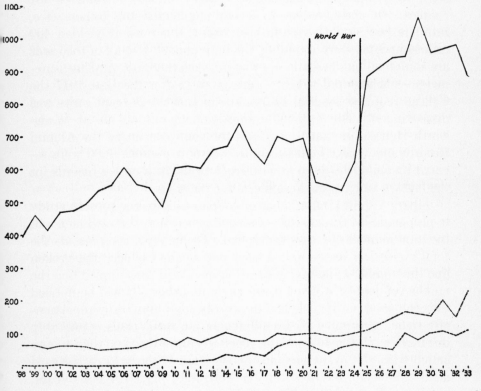

FIG. 1. Number of couples in present study in proportion to the increase of second generation Harvard men and the total number of students

of which was questionable. The final count included 132 fathers who gave measurements for their fathers and 8 who included as well information concerning their grandfathers.

Inasmuch as the material is based entirely on indirect sources and is often in the form of approximation rather than actual measurement, the actual scientific worth is dubious. Probably, however, the most important result is the evidence afforded by the answers to the last question on the questionnaire, "Was your father taller and heavier than you at the age of 19?" The results are shown on pages 18–19.

In summary, the material available from Harvard includes what is designated in the text as a "small series" of 481 couples (400 fathers and their sons) for which 30 measurements and 7 observations are available, and a "large series" for which only heights, weights, and nationalities are available, numbering 1461 couples (1160 fathers and their sons), including the small series for the measurements above mentioned and the information on third and fourth ascending generations secured through letters of inquiry.

In using material from so many sources it seemed advisable to determine if possible the extent to which the factors of "personal equation" and different methods of technique might influence the measurements. Fortunately, in the three main series there was a certain amount of overlapping and a sufficient number of individuals were measured in at least two of the three different sets for adequate comparison. Seventeen couples (i. e. records on the same individual in different series) were compared between the Brigham Register records and the Sargent records. Since weight and stature are the two most significant measurements, and since in the case of the medical records these two factors alone are available, comparisons were restricted to them.

The results of the comparison given in Tables 2 and 3 show that the records are on the whole quite reliable and may be used without correction, since none of the differences are statistically significant. In the case of the fathers the mean coefficient of correlation was found to be .875, in the case of the sons .905. The ages for the fathers and the sons are in both comparisons respectively identical, and the seriations show considerable uniformity.

It has been repeatedly shown [1] that physical measurements are considerably affected by environment, both geographical and sociological, and environment plays a great part in occupation. A survey of the occupations of the fathers of the older generation of Harvard College men shows that the majority were in various professions. Only 10 percent were classed as manual, whereas over 40 percent were lawyers, bankers, business men, or manufacturers

---

[1] See R. Martin, *Lehrbuch der Anthropologie* (2nd edition, 1928), pp. 264–265.

(Table 4). In the case of their sons, i. e. the present generation of Harvard men, the results show interesting changes. The manual class has decreased to less than 2 percent, the lawyers, bankers, business men, and manufacturers constitute over 50 percent, and the class designated as teachers, writers, and artists has exactly doubled, forming in the second group over 17 percent.

TABLE 2

COMPARISON OF RECORDS — FATHERS

Correlations

	No.	r	p. e.
Weight.............	17	.86	.04
Stature	17	.89	.03

Seriations

	Brigham Register					Sargent Cards			
	No.	M	p. e.	σ	p. e.	No.	M	p. e.	σ	p. e.
Age.......	17	20.	.35	2.03	.24	17	20.	.28	1.68	.19
Weight....	17	143.10	2.26	13.80	1.60	17	142.80	2.15	13.10	1.52
Stature ...	17	176.32	.64	3.93	.46	17	174.70	.60	3.63	42

TABLE 3

COMPARISON OF RECORDS — SONS

Correlations

	No.	r	p. e.
Weight.............	50	.93	.01
Stature	50	.88	.02

Seriations

	Sargent Cards					Medical Records			
	No.	M	p. e.	σ	p. e.	No.	M	p. e.	σ	p. e.
Age.......	50	18.60	.10	1.04	.07	50	18.70	.10	1.10	.07
Weight....	50	150.50	1.49	15.70	1.05	50	148.70	1.43	15.10	1.01
Stature ...	50	178.24	.55	5.76	.39	50	177.16	.61	6.42	.43

Although minor changes have affected somewhat the proportions in the different classes, no violent shift has occurred. On the whole we may assume that change of occupation has probably influenced the grandfathers and great-grandfathers of the present generation to a far greater extent than the present students. Unfortunately we can only surmise, from the trend manifested in the two series at our disposal, that the successive ascending generations came in greater proportions from the manual and mercantile classes.   In a later discussion we shall see that the women compare favorably with the men as regards occupational identity of parents.

TABLE 4

OCCUPATIONS OF FATHERS OF HARVARD FATHERS AND SONS

	Fathers		Sons	
	No.	Percent	No.	Percent
Manual workers	34	10.15	8	1.77
Merchants.....................	52	15.52	20	4.42
Scientists and engineers	9	2.69	30	6.62
Doctors and dentists	26	7.76	42	9.27
Lawyers and bankers	83	24.76	163	35.98
Business and manufacturing men	61	18.21	77	17.00
Clerks and civil service men	8	2.40	6	1.32
Clergymen	18	5.37	23	5.08
Teachers, writers, and artists	29	8.66	78	17.22
Retired	15	4.48	6	1.32
Total	335	100.00	453	100.00
Unreported	65		28	
	400		481	

After having given attention to the questions of race and nationality, to the definition of the term Old American, and to occupational change by generations, the next task was to arrange the material in usable form.   For the small series of 481 couples, in order to facilitate comparison and to eliminate the possibility of duplication the measurements from the Brigham Register were put on individual cards of the same size as the Sargent cards, and the order of measurements was correspondingly modified.   The cards of fathers and sons were then selected and fastened together with paper clips, with the father above and the son or sons in order of age beneath, and the pairs or series arranged in groups according to the father's year of birth.   The measurements were then transferred to large sheets of coördinate paper with columns for 30 measurements and 7 observations, together with the ages, names, and card or register numbers.   The arrangement of the fathers born in each year was alphabetical, and under each man was listed his son or sons in order of seniority, so that individual and group comparisons might be made. For the large series, the measurements were transferred directly from the records to the large work sheets, care being taken in each case to see that no duplication of names occurred. The arrangement was again alphabetical and in groups according to the year of the father's birth. The brothers were listed in order of birth.

The first great difficulty was the absence of consideration of the mothers of the sons. It was obviously quite impossible to secure their measurements, since probably only a small percent attended college. Furthermore, even college women were seldom measured until within the past two or three decades. To meet this deficiency it seemed best to get a parallel series, i. e. to secure comparable data (mothers and daughters) from women's colleges.

It will doubtless be argued that even this is hardly satisfactory, since the two sexes are considered separately and no genetic relationship exists between them except their general racial extraction and the uniformity of occupational and cultural background. A further objection lies in the fact that there seems to be a general tendency for men to vary more in their selection of mates than women. If we may suppose, however, that men draw wives more from the Central and Western parts of the United States than formerly, may we not likewise assume that men are quite as likely to come from the same regions and settle in the New England region, the general area under consideration? However that may be, there is no way of meeting the deficiency, which can only be remedied by systematic measurements on a large number of families now, and the measuring of their children and grandchildren at subsequently uniform intervals and at approximately the same ages. The only excuse to be offered is that the best must be made of such materials as are at hand, and they should be used with the reservation that they represent not blood relationships but rather comparable groups, on the physical side in race and age, and on the environmental side in cultural, social, and geographical extraction.

The total number of pairs (mothers and daughters) from the four women's colleges (Wellesley, Vassar, Smith, and Mt. Holyoke) from which data were obtained was 570 (501 mothers and their daughters), distributed as follows:

	Mothers	Daughters
Wellesley	205	241
Vassar	208	227
Smith	53	62
Mt. Holyoke..................	35	40

From the first two institutions, forming four-fifths of the entire series, the measurements are practically identical with the small series for the men's group, while the remaining smaller group of 102 pairs is limited to the two measurements of weight and stature.

The only information available on occupations was for the fathers of the mothers of the present generation of Wellesley College students who themselves had attended Wellesley (Table 5). The resemblance to the equivalent table (Table 4) for the men's series from Harvard is so apparent that we may conclude that all of the student groups under comparison may safely be considered as uniform in this feature.

TABLE 5

Occupations of Fathers of Wellesley College Mothers

	No.	Percent
Manual workers	17	10.49
Merchants.......................	38	23.46
Scientists and engineers	12	7.41
Doctors and dentists	6	3.70
Lawyers and bankers	15	9.25
Business and manufacturing men ...	38	23.46
Clerks and civil service men	10	6.17
Clergymen	17	10.49
Teachers and writers..............	9	5.57
Total	162	100.00
Unreported	43	
	205	

As to race and nationality, from the Wellesley material again the percentage of those designated as American is well over 90 for both mothers and daughters. It appears to be even more true to the Old American standard than that of the men. This may be explained by the fact that college women a generation ago were probably a more selected group than the men, and were consequently largely derived from the older and more established families. Unfortunately no third generation material was available, but this could hardly be expected since measurements in women's colleges are of comparatively recent introduction.

The male and female series have been analyzed first separately and then in comparison with each other. Under the sexes, seriations and correlations are considered respectively; firstly, for the generations, and secondly for those of the same generation. Comparisons from foreign or Old American data are introduced wherever pertinent or necessary for illustration.

Chapter II

MALE STUDENTS

THE material on male students is limited to measurements on Harvard students between the years 1840 and 1930. The study involves a total of nearly 3000 men for the measurements of heights and weights and nearly 1000 men for a series of 30 measurements. It has been the plan throughout, in the analysis of both the male and female series, to compare firstly the generations (sons, fathers, grandfathers, and great-grandfathers in the case of the males, and daughters and mothers in the case of the females), secondly the siblings. The alteration in general type irrespective of relationship is discussed in conjunction with the comparison of generations. Age, statistical constants, unit differences and percentile relations, correlations, indices, and observations are considered in the order named for each generation and for brothers and sisters.

FATHERS AND SONS

AGE

The mean age of all fathers in the large series (1461) is 19.65, and that of the sons 18.51. The standard deviation of the former is 2.26 and of the latter 1.27, while the coefficients of variation are respectively 11.50 and 6.86. The fathers are therefore considerably more variable than the sons as regards age (Table 6).

TABLE 6

COMPARISON OF AGES OF FATHERS AND SONS — LARGE SERIES

	No.	M	σ	V	Range
Fathers	1166	19.65	2.26	11.50	16–34
Sons	1461	18.51	1.27	6.86	15–32

The ages of the small series with 400 fathers and 481 sons are essentially the same as those of the large series; the difference again is only slightly over a year.

The question arises as to the importance of the year's difference in a comparison of the two series. It is quite obvious that neither group has reached maturity, and equally apparent, therefore, that since the sons are the younger due allowance should be made for the discrepancy. It has often been shown, however — and in the present study the conclusions are confirmed — that at least in student groups within certain limits there is no special correlation between age and body measurements. Jackson [1] has shown this to be the case in male and female students of the University of Minnesota, and his explanation is that "the younger college students represent a group precocious physically as well as mentally." Other investigators have also observed the same condition in different institutions.

Correlation of Age with Various Measurements

In the present study the regression of stature upon age is graphically illustrated in Figure 2. The heavy lines represent curves for males (unbroken) and females (broken) of random samples of whites.[2] The unbroken light lines represent the male students (fathers and sons) of the present series and the broken light lines the female students (mothers and daughters). In the case of the former there is little if any rise to be observed, and none comparable with the regular increase of the random sample. From the sixteenth to the nineteenth year there is a slight increase. There is then a decrease to the twenty-third year, and subsequently a secondary tendency towards increase. The lines are practically identical for both fathers and sons. With these may be compared the more or less random samples of the Revolutionary War soldiers (irregular broken line) and the Peabody Ships seamen (stippled line), both of which grouped tend to follow more closely the pattern of the general male population. Quite different is the case in the female students. With both mothers and daughters there is a decided negative correlation from the sixteenth to the twenty-first year, following which there is a slight rise.

The coefficient of correlation for age and weight in the small series is 0 in the case of the sons and barely .16 in the fathers.

[1] C. M. Jackson, *Measurements of Female Students of the University of Minnesota*, American Journal of Physical Anthropology, xii (1930), 363–411.
[2] A. O. Powys, *Data for the Problem of Evolution in Man*, Biometrika, i (1901), 47, modified from Figure 11.

TABLE 7

AGE CORRELATED WITH WEIGHT AND STATURE OF FATHERS AND SONS —
SMALL SERIES

	No.	r	p. e.		No.	r	p. e.
Fathers: Weight ..	399	.16	.03	Sons.......	480	0	
Stature ..	399	−.01	.03		480	−.04	.03

When various other measurements [1] are taken into consideration
and grouped according to types (Table 9), the mean of the coefficients of correlation for the entire series is .01 in the fathers and −.01
in the sons, with an ultimate mean of 0 for the two. It is quite apparent, therefore, that only in a few instances is there any correlation
whatsoever, and that such correlations are offset by negative ones in
other measurements. We may conclude, therefore, that there is no
correlation in student groups between age and bodily measurements.

TABLE 8

AGE CORRELATED WITH WEIGHT AND STATURE OF FATHERS AND SONS —
LARGE SERIES

	No.	r	p. e.		No.	r	p. e.
Fathers Weight ..	1166	.07	.02	Sons.......	1461	.12	.02
Stature ..	1165	.04	.02		1453	.12	.02

TABLE 9

AGE CORRELATED WITH VARIOUS GROUPED MEASUREMENTS OF FATHERS AND
SONS — SMALL SERIES

	Fathers	Sons
Weights	.16	0
Heights and lengths *	0	−.03
Breadths	−.02	0
Girths	.02	0
Total mean	.01	−.01

* Including stature, various heights, lengths of upper and lower arms, foot, and span.

In the large series the coefficients are slightly higher, although in
no case are they significant. The sons have a mean correlation coefficient for age with weight and stature of .12. For the fathers the

[1] The measurements are those given in Tables 17 and 18, and are grouped as in
Table 19.

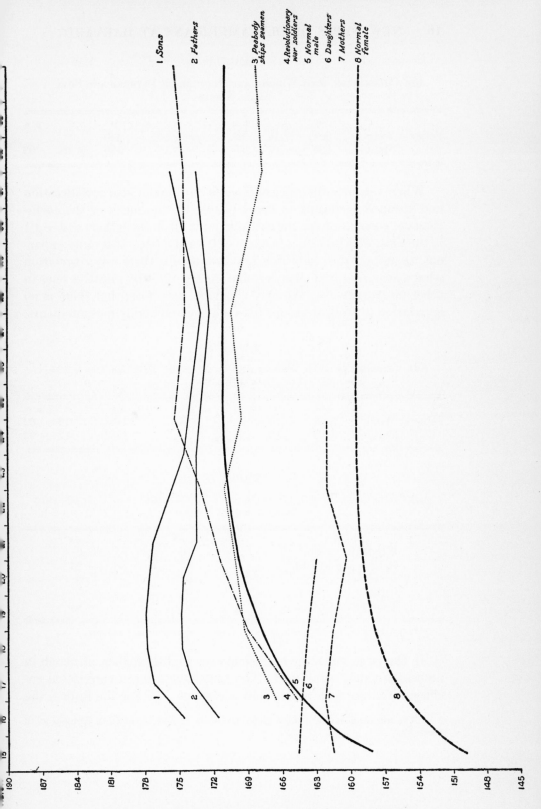

Fig. 2. Regression of stature upon age for males and females

coefficient is .05, or less than half the amount. Even these figures are not statistically significant, and we may take this large sample as a confirmation of the smaller cited above. Tables 10 through 13 give the statistical constants for the small and the large series for the two measurements of weight and stature between the ages 17 and 21.

TABLE 10

WEIGHT OF FATHERS AND SONS AT DIFFERENT AGES — SMALL SERIES *

				Fathers				
Age	No.	M	p. e.	σ	p. e.	V	p. e.	Range
17	32	133.42	1.94	16.33	1.37	12.24	1.03	111–165.5
18	86	135.40	1.03	14.13	.72	10.44	.53	106–172
19	88	139.49	.96	13.35	.67	9.57	.48	107–186
20	48	145.00	1.75	18.06	1.25	12.46	.86	110–217
21	51	145.98	1.41	15.04	1.01	10.30	.69	118–177.5

				Sons				
Age	No.	M	p. e.	σ	p. e.	V	p. e.	Range
17	66	148.63	1.32	15.85	.94	10.66	.63	115.5–183.5
18	170	149.56	.80	15.37	.57	10.28	.38	113.5–207.5
19	139	151.96	1.05	18.45	.74	12.14	.49	116.0–200
20	62	150.74	1.54	17.70	1.06	11.74	.70	124.5–211
21	19	153.32	2.81	18.12	1.94	11.82	1.25	127.5–206

* In all tables, unless otherwise indicated, weights are in pounds and linear measurements in centimeters.

TABLE 11

STATURE OF FATHERS AND SONS AT DIFFERENT AGES — SMALL SERIES

				Fathers				
Age	No.	M	p. e.	σ	p. e.	V	p. e.	Range
17	32	174.19	.82	6.87	.58	3.94	.33	158.5–186
18	86	173.26	.47	6.49	.33	3.75	.19	159.5–191
19	87	173.83	.43	5.92	.30	3.41	.17	153.5–188
20	49	174.54	.50	5.19	.35	2.97	.20	163.0–184
21	51	173.13	.51	5.44	.36	3.14	.21	159.5–184

				Sons				
Age	No.	M	p. e.	σ	p. e.	V	p. e.	Range
17	66	176.71	.52	6.22	.37	3.52	.21	163.0–194.5
18	170	177.78	.28	5.38	.20	3.03	.11	163.0–189.5
19	139	177.77	.36	6.32	.25	3.56	.14	159.5–192
20	62	177.07	.53	6.15	.37	3.47	.21	161.5–189
21	19	174.58	.75	4.84	.53	2.77	.30	168.0–184

TABLE 12

WEIGHT OF FATHERS AND SONS AT DIFFERENT AGES — LARGE SERIES

Fathers

Age	No.	M	p. e.	σ	p. e.	V	p. e.	Range
17	89	135.70	1.16	16.10	.81	11.86	.60	101–190
18	281	139.40	.71	17.70	.50	12.70	.36	100–220
19	323	142.00	.65	17.10	.46	12.04	.33	100–220
20	177	146.60	1.00	19.70	.71	13.44	.48	90–220
21	99	143.50	1.14	16.70	.80	11.64	.56	100–190

Sons

Age	No.	M	p. e.	σ	p. e.	V	p. e.	Range
17	218	145.70	.82	17.90	.57	12.29	.39	100–210
18	531	149.00	.50	17.40	.37	11.68	.25	100–210
19	444	150.40	.59	18.30	.42	12.17	.28	100–250
20	164	151.10	1.00	18.90	.70	12.51	.46	100–220
21	53	151.40	1.53	16.50	1.09	10.90	.72	110–210

TABLE 13

STATURE OF FATHERS AND SONS AT DIFFERENT AGES — LARGE SERIES

Fathers

Age	No.	M	p. e.	σ	p. e.	V	p. e.	Range
17	89	173.72	.45	6.28	.32	3.62	.18	154–186
18	281	174.04	.24	6.08	.17	3.49	.10	158–194
19	322	·174.84	.29	6.32	.17	3.61	.10	154–198
20	178	174.56	.30	5.80	.21	3.32	.12	154–190
21	98	173.28	.38	5.56	.27	3.21	.15	158–186

Sons

Age	No.	M	p. e.	σ	p. e.	V	p. e.	Range
17	217	176.92	.32	6.60	.24	3.73	.11	154–198
18	528	177.68	.19	6.44	.14	3.62	.08	150–194
19	442	177.80	.21	6.64	.15	3.73	.09	150–202
20	163	177.28	.37	6.92	.26	3.90	.14	150–198
21	52	177.16	.65	6.96	.46	3.93	.26	154–194

The subject of the correlation between age and different measurements is further discussed in connection with female students, in whom there is in most instances a negative result, with the ultimate mean coefficient of −.04 for all measurements for mothers and daughters combined (Table 94).

For comparison with the population at large, the data on the Revolutionary War soldiers may be taken as a fair sample. The soldiers were selected quite at random, the ages ranging from 15 to 50. In this instance the coefficient of correlation between age and stature is .30, as opposed to that of −.12 in the rather highly selected group of seamen. The mean age of both groups is 24½ years.

TABLE 14

COEFFICIENT OF CORRELATION OF AGE AND STATURE FOR PEABODY SHIPS SEAMEN AND REVOLUTIONARY WAR SOLDIERS

	No.	r	p. e.
Seamen	225	−.12	.04
Soldiers	315	.30	.04

Grouped at intervals of five years the soldiers show steady increase in all three categories (Table 15). The sailors, on the other hand, are very nearly the same as regards height, and show evident selection of rather short even-statured men (Table 16).

TABLE 15

STATURE OF REVOLUTIONARY WAR SOLDIERS GROUPED AT FIVE YEAR AGE INTERVALS

Ages	No.	M	p. e.	σ	p. e.	V	p. e.	Range
15–20	96	168.01	.39	5.67	.28	3.37	.17	145–178
21–25	110	170.86	.43	6.66	.30	3.90	.18	154–190
26–30	56	175.21	.47	5.22	.33	2.98	.19	163–187
Over 30	53	....	..	....	..	....	..	....
Total *........	315	172.51	.24	6.30	.17	3.65	.10	145–190

TABLE 16

STATURE OF PEABODY SHIPS SEAMEN GROUPED AT FIVE YEAR AGE INTERVALS

Ages	No.	M	p. e.	σ	p. e.	V	p. e.	Range
15–20	67	169.39	.44	5.31	.31	3.14	.18	160–181
21–25	59	170.35	.60	6.84	.42	4.02	.25	154–190
26–30	56	169.69	.56	6.27	.40	3.69	.24	157–187
Over 30	43	....	..	....	..	....	..	....
Total *........	225	169.21	.28	6.33	.20	3.74	.12	154–190

* Including those over 30 years of age.

Powys [1] has shown that stature increases in males till the twenty-seventh year, after which there is a gradual decrease till death at the rate of about one inch every thirty years, or .08 centimeters per annum. For females the maximum is reached about the twenty-fifth year and the subsequent decrease is approximately the same. In the case of the soldiers, therefore, had those above the age of 27 been excluded the coefficient might have been even higher.

We may summarize the results as follows: (1) there is no correlation between age and body measurements among student classes nor among any rather highly selected groups such as represented by the Peabody Ships seamen; (2) there is significant positive correlation in males between age and stature up to the twenty-seventh year in unselected groups such as the series of Soldiers of the Revolutionary War.

COMPARISON OF STATISTICAL CONSTANTS OF 30 MEASUREMENTS

The various measurements recorded by or under the direction of Dr. D. A. Sargent include many which are very serviceable in making comparisons between the two generations, the sons of Harvard men now in college and their fathers. The measurements are directly comparable, since an age difference of only one year exists between the two generations, and, as has been noted, there is no correlation in student groups between age and body measurements. Unfortunately, the only head measurements recorded are breadth, girth, and, in the case of the sons, length, and it is thus possible to make only a rough estimate of the cephalic index in the case of the fathers. Various statistical constants for the measurements are listed in Tables 17 and 18.

In all instances except breadth of head, breadth of hips, and shoulder-elbow length there is an increase of the sons' over the fathers' measurements. The statistical constants are somewhat variable but are more nearly equal than might be expected. Grouped according to types of measurements the standard deviations and coefficients of variation are given in Table 19.

The sons have a slightly higher mean standard deviation, although the coefficient of variation is higher in the fathers.

In comparing the various measurements of fathers and sons it seemed advisable not to compare each of the measurements indi-

[1] 1901.

vidually but to take only the most significant ones — stature, weight, sitting height, knee height and pubic height, navel height and sternal height, span, foot length, arm length, length and breadth of head,

TABLE 17

MEASUREMENTS OF FATHERS — SMALL SERIES

	No.	M	p. e.	σ	p. e.	V	p. e.	Range
Weight.............	399	140.24	.55	16.22	.39	11.57	.28	104 −200
Stature	399	173.95	.20	6.00	.14	3.45	.08	153 −191
Sitting height	350	90.95	.11	3.00	.08	3.30	.08	82 −100
Knee height	399	46.66	.10	2.81	.07	6.02	.14	39 − 57
Pubic height	399	87.10	.15	4.36	.10	5.01	.12	76 −102
Navel height........	399	103.72	.16	4.79	.11	4.62	.11	86.5−118.5
Sternal height.......	399	141.83	.18	5.31	.13	3.79	.09	125 −159
Girth of neck	398	34.70	.06	1.69	.04	4.87	.12	30 − 40
Girth of chest (N) ..	398	86.88	.19	5.68	.14	6.54	.16	72 −110
Girth of chest (F) ...	397	91.88	.19	5.60	.13	6.10	.15	78 −114
Girth of waist.......	397	72.88	.18	5.38	.13	7.44	.18	60 − 98
Girth of hips........	395	89.28	.16	4.82	.12	5.40	.13	78 −112
Girth of thigh.......	397	52.12	.12	3.56	.09	6.83	.16	44 − 67
Girth of knee	396	35.52	.06	1.89	.05	5.32	.13	31 − 43
Girth of calf	399	35.09	.07	2.18	.05	6.21	.15	30 − 43
Girth of upper arm ..	479*	29.37	.08	2.51	.06	8.55	.19	23 − 37
Girth of elbow	472*	25.17	.05	1.45	.03	5.76	.13	21 − 29
Girth of forearm	479*	25.78	.05	1.74	.04	6.75	.15	21 − 33
Girth of wrist	479*	16.23	.03	.89	.02	5.48	.12	14 − 18.5
Breadth of head	396	153†	.19	5.50	.13	3.59	.09	135 −170
Breadth of neck	477*	10.94	.02	.73	.016	6.67	.15	13.5− 17
Breadth of shoulders	476*	42.69	.07	2.25	.05	5.27	.12	9 − 12.5
Breadth of waist	478*	25.33	.05	1.73	.04	6.83	.15	36 − 51
Breadth of hips	479*	33.06	.05	1.57	.03	4.75	.10	20 − 32
Breadth between nipples	476*	20.26	.05	1.64	.04	8.09	.18	29 − 40
Shoulder-elbow length	477*	37.55	.05	1.75	.04	4.66	.10	33 − 44
Elbow-finger length .	474*	46.92	.06	1.97	.04	4.20	.09	41 − 52
Length of foot	477*	25.98	.04	1.23	.03	4.73	.10	21.5− 29.5
Span...............	474*	178.20	.21	6.92	.15	3.88	.09	159 −198

* Calculated from the correlation tables, and consequently duplicating the fathers where there was more than one son (cf. Coefficients of Correlation, p. 54).
† Millimeters.

girth measurements, and breadth measurements — and to compare the remainder under the general subject of unit differences and percentile relationships (p. 52). In the following pages, therefore, the various measurements are discussed in the order mentioned.

TABLE 18

MEASUREMENTS OF SONS — SMALL SERIES

	No.	M	p. e.	σ	p. e.	V	p. e.	Range
Weight.............	480	150.30	.53	17.20	.38	11.44	.25	107 –215
Stature	480	177.50	.19	6.04	.13	3.40	.07	158 –196
Sitting height	479	92.14	.18	5.70	.13	6.19	.14	79 –102
Knee height	478	47.02	.08	2.54	.06	5.40	.12	38 – 56
Pubic height	478	89.02	.13	4.06	.09	4.56	.10	76 –100
Navel height........	478	107.02	.14	4.67	.10	4.36	.10	84.5–120
Sternal height.......	478	145.10	.16	5.13	.11	3.60	.08	132 –161
Length of head......	475	194.13*.25		8.20	.18	4.22	.09	170 –215
Girth of neck	478	35.64	.05	1.56	.03	4.38	.10	32 – 41
Girth of chest (N) ..	479	90.88	.08	2.70	.06	2.97	.07	75 –110
Girth of chest (F) ...	477	94.38	.17	5.60	.12	5.93	.14	83 –116
Girth of waist.......	478	73.48	.15	4.94	.11	6.72	.15	61 – 94
Girth of hips........	476	91.84	.14	4.64	.10	5.05	.11	77 –114
Girth of thigh.......	478	53.94	.11	3.62	.08	6.71	.15	44 – 69
Girth of knee	478	36.62	.06	1.96	.04	5.35	.12	31 – 44
Girth of calf	479	35.59	.06	2.08	.05	5.84	.13	30 – 44
Girth of upper arm ..	479	30.78	.07	2.38	.05	7.73	.17	25 – 40
Girth of elbow	472	25.46	.04	1.34	.03	5.26	.12	22 – 31
Girth of forearm	479	26.80	.05	1.56	.03	5.82	.13	22 – 33
Girth of wrist.......	479	16.42	.03	.84	.02	5.12	.11	14 – 19
Breadth of head	475	150.09*.17		5.60	.12	3.71	.08	130 –170
Breadth of neck	477	11.17	.02	.61	.01	5.46	.12	13 – 17
Breadth of shoulders	476	43.68	.07	2.19	.05	5.01	.11	9.5– 13
Breadth of waist	478	25.90	.06	1.80	.04	6.95	.15	38 – 49
Breadth of hips	479	32.92	.05	1.71	.04	5.19	.11	21 – 34
Breadth between nipples	476	20.34	.05	1.55	.03	7.62	.17	27 – 40
Shoulder-elbow length	477	36.80	.05	1.68	.04	4.57	.10	32 – 41
Elbow-finger length .	474	47.93	.06	1.90	.04	3.96	.09	42 – 53
Length of foot	477	26.15	.04	1.22	.03	4.67	.10	22.5– 30
Span..............	474	181.98	.21	6.62	.15	3.64	.08	159 –200

* Millimeters.

TABLE 19

COMPARISON OF GROUPED MEASUREMENTS OF FATHERS AND SONS — SMALL SERIES

	σ		V	
	Fathers	Sons	Fathers	Sons
Weight............	16.22	17.20	11.57	11.44
Heights and lengths	3.81	3.96	4.37	4.44
Girths	3.15	2.77	6.28	5.57
Breadths	2.23	2.24	5.86	4.37
Mean	6.35	6.56	7.02	6.45

Stature

In the small series of the present study the mean stature of the fathers is 173.95 ±.20 centimeters, with a standard deviation of 6.00 and a coefficient of variability of 3.45. The sons measure 177.50 ±.19 centimeters, with deviation 6.04 and variation 3.40. The fathers are 3.55 centimeters shorter than their sons, are equally as variable, and in proportion are 98 percent as tall.[1]

The question at once arises as to whether this decided change is due to genetic factors operating from within or to environmental factors influencing from without.

Already in 1906 Sargent [2] had noted an increase in stature and weight. In 1880 he found among Harvard students a mean of 172.00 centimeters; in 1906 the mean was 174.50. The weights were correspondingly 135.2 pounds and 139.2–143.2 pounds (see Table 20). Concerning the difference he makes no suggestion of possible causes except physical exercise, and merely comments, "This is a most remarkable uplift in growth and development for any considerable body of men in any country or community to have attained in twenty-five years."

TABLE 20

INCREASE IN STATURE AND WEIGHT (1880–1906) — SARGENT

Years	No.	Stature	Weight
1880	1000	172.00	135.20
1906	1035	174.50	139.20–143.2
Difference		2.50	6.00

Since Sargent's discovery numerous subsequent investigators in this country have also noticed the same phenomenon, as have many in European countries before him. In no instance, however, has the amount of annual increase been determined, nor have satisfactory causes been advanced.

[1] In the large series the statistical constants for the two generations are:

	No.	M	p. e.	σ	p. e.	V	p. e.	Range
Sons...........	1453	177.76	.12	5.88	.08	3.31	.04	150–199
Fathers........	1165	174.37	.12	6.04	.08	3.46	.05	154–196
Difference		3.39						

[2] D. A. Sargent, *The Physique of Scholars, Athletes, and the Average Student*, Popular Science Monthly, LXXIII (1908), 248–256.

In the present study, in order to determine the nature and amount of the increase, all of the students in the large series, i. e. the fathers and sons combined, were considered as a single group of representative Old Americans, sorted according to years of birth, and arranged by decades. Table 21 shows the various means and statistical constants for the different decade groups.

TABLE 21

STATURE OF MALE STUDENTS BY BIRTH DECADES — LARGE SERIES

	No.	M	p. e.	σ	p. e.	V	p. e.	Range
1836–45	2	170.50	2.86	6.00	2.02	3.52	.80	166–178
1846–55	43	174.13	.50	4.86	.35	2.79	.20	166–187
1856–65	335	172.90	.22	6.06	.16	3.51	.09	157–196
1866–75	506	174.40	.18	6.00	.13	3.44	.07	157–193
1876–85	307	175.60	.23	5.94	.16	3.38	.09	160–196
1886–95	267	176.32	.26	6.45	.19	3.66	.11	154–193
1896–05	607	177.28	.17	6.39	.12	3.61	.07	157–196
1906–15	546	178.03	.20	6.72	.13	3.77	.08	151–199

Between each decade after the year 1855 there is consistent increase, till the final stature in the last category reaches 178.03 centimeters. The small numbers employed in the first two decades probably account for the high figures. In order to increase the numbers in the first two decades so that they might be favorably compared with the others, additional data from class records and the Brigham Register were employed, with the result that the means were changed to the following:

	No.	M
1836–45	550*	172.49
1846–55	1089*	173.34

* The numbers are not definite, inasmuch as the frequencies in the class records were not always given.

With this supplementary data the total period covered is 80 years, or nearly three generations, during which, with the exception of a slight drop in the decade 1856–65, there is steady and quite marked increase. Thus we may establish that it is not because a man is a son that he is taller but because he was born later than his father. The causes, whatever they may be, have nothing to do with generations but with the date of birth, which controls numerous subsidiary factors to be discussed in detail later.

In Table 22 the differences between the various decades are arranged and the mean annual increase for each period is computed.

It will be seen that the amount of annual increase varies considerably with each decade. Barring the first two, however, there is a perceptible decrease between 1856 and 1896 from .15 centimeters to .07, i. e. to less than half the original figure. We may conclude, therefore, that the annual increase is gradually lessening, having reached its height in the two decades 1856–75. When averaged, the mean annual increase is .08 for the 80 year period — one centimeter every 12½ years or one inch every 32 years.

Compared statistically the results are even more interesting. The usual determination of significance, that the difference between the two means must be at least three times the square root of the

TABLE 22

INCREASE OF STATURE FOR MALE STUDENTS BY BIRTH DECADES — LARGE SERIES

	1836–45*	1846–55	1856–65	1866–75	1876–85	1886–95	1896–05
1846–55*	.85	....					
1856–65	.41	−.44	....				
1866–75	1.91	1.06	1.50	....			
1876–85	3.11	2.26	2.70	1.20	....		
1886–95	3.83	2.98	3.42	1.92	.72	....	
1896–05	4.79	3.94	4.38	2.88	1.68	.96	....
1906–15	5.54	4.69	5.13	3.63	2.43	1.71	.75
Annual increase .	.08	−.04	.15	.12	.07	.10	.07

Mean annual increase .08

* Using corrected figures.

sum of the squares of the probable errors of the means, is accepted here. Dividing the difference by the derived square root probable error we have convenient figures for comparison.

Reducing for comparative purposes and omitting the first two decades, for which means alone are given and for which consequently the amounts cannot be calculated, we have the results presented in Table 23.

The mean figure 3.48 is thus significant, and from it we may deduce that a statistically significant increase (3 times the probable error) is to be noted every 8½ years.

Comparative data for this increase in stature are very scarce on American students. There is plenty of material which would in bulk amount to several thousands of individuals, and were the authors cited there would be an impressive list. In no two cases, however, are conditions the same. The earlier work of Dickson invariably measures "with shoes," and the age variation is between 20 and 30, far too great a range for satisfactory results. Gould, Allen, Hitchcock and Seelye, Sargent, Cattelland, Farrand, Hastings, Seaver, Elsom, Meylan, Raycroft, Jackson, and others have all recorded data, but in no instance is the material clearly and definitely designated as Old American; in most cases the only distinction is "mostly native." Geographical variations are not recorded, and parental occupations are seldom considered. In short, in very few instances are the data in any way comparable with those of the present study.

TABLE 23

DIFFERENCES OF STATURE IN TERMS OF THE PROBABLE ERROR FOR MALE STUDENTS BY BIRTH DECADES — LARGE SERIES

	1836–45	1846–55	1856–65	1866–75	1876–85	1886–95	1896–05
1846–55	....	....					
1856–65	....	....	....				
1866–75	....	....	5.29	....			
1876–85	....	....	8.54	4.11	....		
1886–95	....	....	10.30	6.07	2.07	....	
1896–05	....	....	15.85	11.61	5.69	3.09	....
1906–15	....	....	17.27	12.74	7.96	5.21	2.86

Mean figure for contiguous decades 3.48

The extreme variations in measurements are thus largely to be accounted for on grounds of heterogeneity of material, and the only way in which suitable comparisons can be made is to take separately each college for which there is adequate material and determine the changes locally. These changes may be compared with the present material and some reason be brought out of the otherwise confused and unrelated data.

For Amherst [1] between the years 1861 and 1889 we have the following figures:

TABLE 24

STATURE OF AMHERST STUDENTS (1861–89)

Data	No.	Age	Stature
1861–69	....	20–23	172.2
1861–88	670	16–26	172.5
1860–90	1280	18–25	173.2
1884–89	2000	21	172.7

[1] E. Hitchcock and H. H. Seelye, *Statistics Bearing upon the Average and Typical Student in Amherst College*, Journal of the Anthropological Institute, XVII (1888), 357–358, and XVIII, 192–199.

The ages here are so variable that it is difficult to determine the extent of annual increase. In the late nineties there seems even to have been a slight drop.

For Princeton University Wissler [1] gives the following figures:

TABLE 25

STATURE OF PRINCETON STUDENTS (1911–15)

1911 .... 174.3	1912........ 175.4	1915........ 175.7

For the 5 year period there was an increase of 1.4 centimeters, or a mean annual increase of .28 centimeters, but no frequencies are given and the period covered is too short to serve as a satisfactory sample.

At Pennsylvania University, according to latest figures of the registrar, stature has increased from 171.20 to 172.72, or 1.52 centimeters, over a period of 20 years (1910–30), with a mean annual increase of .076, or .08 centimeters, practically identical with the increase at Harvard. Weight during the same period has increased from 132 to 140 pounds, with a mean annual increase of .40 pounds — again very close to the increase at Harvard.[2] Age has decreased from 19.6 to 18.5. Similar increases have been noted at Yale, Wisconsin, and other men's colleges in the East and Midwest.

Non-student Old American material comparable in age is equally difficult to secure. In fact, outside of Army measurements, where racial connections are rather obscure, sources are extremely limited. In the present study a series of 315 soldiers of the Revolutionary War from New Hampshire [3] (born between the years 1725 and 1765 and averaging 24.5 years of age) showed a mean stature of 172.51.[4] Arranged by decades according to years of birth there was no relationship or increase. The reason is quite obvious when the ages are compared, for the 19 year old subadults in such a random sample should fall considerably below the figure for the 26 or 37 year old mature men. In the 48 year old group the mean drops nearly a centimeter, as would be expected.

[1] C. Wissler, *Relation of Nature to Man in Aboriginal North America* (1926), p. 147.
[2] Cf. Table 43.
[3] Rolls of the Soldiers in the Revolutionary War, New Hampshire State Papers, vol. II, Concord, New Hampshire.
[4] Including Colonel Jos. Cillery's Regiment and absentees belonging to the 1st New Hampshire Regiment, Valley Forge, January 10, 1778. No statement is made in regard to method of measurement. Consequently no allowance for shoes is made. The mean has not been corrected for any factor.

TABLE 26

STATURE OF REVOLUTIONARY WAR SOLDIERS BY BIRTH DECADES

Years	No.	Age	M	p. e.	σ	p. e.	V	p. e.	Range
1726–35	12	48	174.25	.68	3.51	.48	2.01	.28	169–184
1736–45	34	37	175.15	.63	5.43	.45	3.10	.25	163–184
1746–55	131	26	174.91	.34	5.73	.24	3.28	.14	160–187
1756–65	138	19	169.51	.36	6.24	.26	3.68	.15	142–184
Total	315	24.5	172.51						

Far more homogeneous, but still showing the characteristic rise to full maturity and subsequent shrinkage, is the series of sailors from the Peabody Ships. The mean average, 169.21, is significantly lower than the mean for the soldiers (172.51), and is probably due, as above suggested, to the desire to secure short men. In comparable age groups, however, the sailors are slightly but not significantly taller.

TABLE 27

STATURE OF PEABODY SHIPS SEAMEN BY BIRTH DECADES

Years	No.	Age	M	p. e.	σ	p. e.	V	p. e.	Range
1766–75	10	44	164.50	1.57	7.35	1.10	4.47	.67	154–178
1776–85	63	31	168.52	1.01	11.88	.71	7.05	.42	157–184
1786–95	134	22	170.14	.37	6.30	.26	3.70	.15	157–190
1796–05	18	18	168.55	.89	5.43	.63	3.22	.37	160–181
Total	225	24.5	169.21						

For the sake of arriving at some conclusion in regard to increase in stature over a longer period than that covered by students alone (80 years), the soldiers and sailors similar in type have been included in a comparative table (Table 28). Those included are of the same extraction geographically and racially as the students, and of approximately the same age, differing from them only in occupation.

The annual increase over a period of 150 years, or nearly five generations, calculated from the difference between the two pole means (8.52 centimeters), is .058 centimeters, or roughly .06 centimeters, .02 centimeters under the figure for Harvard students as a whole. All of the various groups concerned in the present study are seriated by years of measurement in Table 29.

TABLE 28

STATURE BY BIRTH DECADES BETWEEN THE AGES 18 AND 22 — ALL SERIES

Years	No.	Age	M	p. e.	Range	Series
1756–65	138	19.0	169.51	.36	142–184	Soldiers
1766–75	..	..	..	..	..	....
1776–85	..	..	..	..	..	....
1786–95	134	22.0	170.14	.37	157–190	Seamen
1796–05	..	..	..	..	..	....
1806–15	..	..	..	..	..	....
1816–25	..	..	..	..	..	....
1826–35	..	..	..	..	..	....
1836–45	550*	21.0	172.49	..	..	Students
1846–55	1089*	22.0	173.34	..	..	"
1856–65	335	22.0	172.90	..	..	"
1866–75	506	19.6	174.40	..	..	"
1876–85	307	19.6	175.60	..	..	"
1886–95	267	19.0	176.32	..	..	"
1896–05	607	18.5	177.28	..	..	"
1906–15	546	18.5	178.03	..	..	"

* Includes measurements for class records and Brigham Register records.

TABLE 29

STATURE OF VARIOUS SERIES IN PRESENT STUDY COMPARED

	Years	No.	Age	M
Revolutionary War soldiers	1778	315	24.5	172.51
Peabody Ships seamen	1811–15	225	24.5	169.21
Class records	1860–80	1870	22.0	172.99
Brigham Register records	1870–72	140	23.0	173.33
Fathers of large series	1875–10	1166	19.6	174.37
Sons of large series	1905–29	1461	18.5	177.76

We may summarize the results on stature as follows: (1) Sons are absolutely taller than their fathers. (2) In the student population for at least the past 80 years and probably longer there has been marked annual increase. The rate has varied, reaching the peak in those born between 1860 and 1870, when the mean annual increase was .15, and dropping in those born between 1905 and 1910, when the increase was .07. (3) The mean annual rate of increase for the entire student population for the past 80 years has been approximately one centimeter every 12½ years, statistical significance occurring every 8½ years. (4) For the population as a whole the figure is somewhat smaller but is probably between .06 and .07 centimeters per annum. (5) The mean stature of the present-day Old American student population in Massachusetts and vicinity is 178.03 centimeters, rating thus among the tallest people observed anywhere and 4 centimeters or more above the population as a whole. (6) There is no significant correlation between age and stature among students between the usual college ages of 17 and 23. (7) The increase in one generation, approximately 35 years, has been 3.55 centimeters, or about 1¼ inches.

In fine, throughout the country as a whole, and more especially in New England, there has been marked increase in the stature of Old Americans over a statistically observed period of 150 years. This increase, .06 centimeters in the population at large and about .08 centimeters for students, reached its peak in those born about the year 1865 or shortly after the Civil War, and has since somewhat declined, the present rate being probably about .05 centimeters for the general population and .07 centimeters for the students. At the present rate of decrease in annual increment equilibrium should be reached during the next 50 years when the stature will be well over 180 centimeters.

Increase in Stature as a World Phenomenon

In the following few pages the most outstanding examples of stature increase as a world phenomenon are selected in an endeavor to determine the rate of increase, its present importance, and the significance it may have for the future. Apology must be made for the scanty data. Examples from Norway, Sweden, Denmark, Germany, Holland, Switzerland, Italy, Spain, and Japan are considered in the order named.

The earliest work on *Norwegians* [1] was by Surgeon General Heiberg, who of his own initiative measured conscripts of 22 years of age over a 5 year period (1855–59). Arbo (1895) arranged the tables and determined the mean at 168.6 centimeters.

The efforts of de Besche (1872), Arbo (1903), Waaler (1923) and Schreiner (1929) have afforded quite ample data for the past fifty years.

By using the earlier material of Waaler and additional data from the official recruit statistics Schreiner discovered that increase in stature was steady up to 1923, but that in the two succeeding years there was a slight decrease (Tables 30 and 31).

[1] Modified from Bryn and Schreiner, *Somatologie der Norweger* (1929), Table 11, p. 28; see also pp. 25–29.

TABLE 30

MEAN STATURE OF NORWEGIAN CONSCRIPTS (1878–1925)

Years	No.	Age	M	Authority
1855–59	....	22	168.60	Heiberg
1878–87	....	22	168.80	Arbo
1888–97	....	22	169.30	"
1898–02	67,398	22	170.39	Schreiner
1903–07	64,668	22	170.79	"
1908–12	76,778	22	171.15	"
1913–17	118,729	22	171.31	"
1918–22	111,667	22	171.46	"
1923–25	68,683	22	171.81	"

TABLE 31

MEAN STATURE OF NORWEGIAN CONSCRIPTS ANNUALLY (1899–1925)

Years	No.	Age	M
1899	13,975	22	170.27
1900	14,107	22	170.43
1901	13,716	22	170.40
1902	13,934	22	170.58
1903	12,854	22	170.62
1904	12,109	22	170.59
1905	12,875	22	170.58
1906	12,826	22	170.77
1907	14,004	22	170.94
1908	14,191	22	170.86
1909	14,495	22	170.99
1910	15,708	22	171.19
1911	14,984	22	171.33
1912	17,400	22	171.31
1913	16,265	22 and 21	171.37
1914	19,341	22 and 21	171.43
1915	19,966	22 and 21	171.23
1916	40,715	22, 21, and 20	171.37
1917	22,442	21 and 20	171.09
1918	20,565	20	171.28
1919	21,522	20	171.31
1920	21,977	20	171.42
1921	23,944	20	171.52
1922	23,659	20	171.72
1923	23,620	20	171.84
1924	23,648	20	171.82
1925	23,415	20	171.76

Arranged by periods, the annual increase varies considerably. From 1878 to 1897, over two periods of ten years each it was .05 centimeters, from 1898 to 1902, .21 centimeters, and in the following three 5 year periods .05, .06, and .04 centimeters respectively. The greatest increase occurred at the close of the last century.

The conclusion is that "the young men of today are, at the age of 20, on the whole 3 centimeters taller than their fathers at 22 years." A further conclusion is reached, that the Norwegians of the Middle Ages were considerably taller than those of the Stone Age.

In various parts of Norway, again, the rate of increase has not been uniform. The most striking difference from the mean is noted from the northernmost province, Finnmark, where there is a high percentage of Lapps. Here Schreiner found that the increase was more marked than for the country as a whole.

Schreiner explains this on the basis of the improved economic and hygienic conditions under which the Lapp Norwegian mixed peoples live. He believes that changed conditions influenced Finnmark more than the country at large.

This explanation of the differences seems hardly justifiable, unless we suppose the changes in Finnmark to be far greater and far more effective than for the entire country. It would seem more plausible to look for a solution from the racial viewpoint. Schreiner has stated, either as a fact or by implication, that there are Lapp mixtures. It would seem, therefore, that part of the explanation for the phenomenon may be found in hybrid vigor or similar genetic causes of accentuated growth.

For *Sweden*, statistics for recruits between 1841 and 1870 are given by Arbo (1875), who finds the following increases:

TABLE 32

STATURE OF SWEDISH RECRUITS (1841-70)

Years	M
1841-45	167.36*
1846-50	167.40
1851-55	167.81
1856-60	168.06
1861-65	168.53
1866-70	169.60
Increase ...... 2.24 Annual increase ...... .077	

* Lundborg and Linders, *Anthropology of Sweden* (1926), p. 61.

Supplementing the earlier work of Arbo, Lundborg and Linders [1] give the following table for recruits of 21 years of age:

TABLE 33

STATURE OF SWEDISH RECRUITS (1887–1922)

Years	M
1887–90	169.20
1890–95	169.60
1896–00	170.10
1901–05	170.80
1906–10	171.60
1911–15	172.00
1916–20	171.70
1921–22	171.90

The above is compiled from official statistics, and although the numbers are not given it is safe to presume that the frequencies would be quite adequate for use as comparative data.

There is also a difference between the measurements of Retzius and Furst [2] and those of Lundborg and Linders. The former authorities in 1902 found a mean for the entire country of 170.88, whereas in 1926 the mean had risen to 172.23, an increase of 1.35 centimeters in a quarter of a century.

The latter writers have elaborate tables showing the unit and percental increases over the same period for each of the landskaps. The most striking gains are primarily in the urban sections and secondarily in the central regions, with the southern section intermediate, and the gains in the northern region slightly less than in the southern. It is hard to account for the reversal in the case of Sweden of what occurred in Norway, where the northernmost province with the larger percentage of Lapp and Finn population showed the greatest gains. The explanation probably lies in the relative extent of betterment of living conditions and the degree of racial miscegenation.

In *Denmark* the increase, although not so great as in the case of Holland, is comparable with the other Scandinavian countries. Over a period of 53 years there was an increase of 3.69 centimeters, showing a mean annual increase of .07 centimeters. There is no indication of any local variations in the different districts.

[1] 1926, p. 61.
[2] G. Retzius and C. M. Furst, *Anthropologica Suecica* (1902).

A comparison of Norwegian, Swedish, and Danish conscripts of the same age between 1918 and 1925 showed that the mean annual increase was greatest for the Swedish and least for the Danish. The total increases noted for the three were respectively .58 centimeters or .339 percent, .75 centimeters or .436 percent, and .40 centimeters or .243 percent. In the case of Sweden, however, there was in 1926 a drop to 172.53 centimeters. Figures for the other countries had not been computed for this year.

TABLE 34

STATURE OF ADULT DANES * (1852–1905)

Years	M
1852–56	165.42
1879–88	167.78
1891–00	168.43
1904–05	169.11
Increase 3.69	Annual increase ...... .069

* From Bryn and Schreiner (1929), p. 29 (after Mackeprang, 1907).

In *Germany* data are not so complete. At Frankfurt, Meinhausen (1921) found an increase between 1892 and 1912 of 1.2 centimeters.[1] Reduced to annual increase, the figure is not especially high, .06 centimeters, and is less than that for Old Americans of the same period (Table 28).

TABLE 35

STATURE OF 19-YEAR-OLD DUTCH CONSCRIPTS (1863–1925)

Period	M	Authority
1863–67	164.10	Bruinsma
1868–72	164.50	"
1873–77	164.90	"
1878–82	165.20	"
1883–87	165.60	"
1888–92	166.40	"
1893–97	166.00	"
1898–07	166.80	Bolk, v. d. Broek
1907–	169.05	Bolk
1921–25	170.77	v. d. Broek
Increase 6.67	Annual increase .172	

[1] Martin (1928), pp. 263-264.

In *Holland* the increase has been even greater than in the case of the Scandinavian countries. Between the years 1863 and 1925, a period of 62 years, there was an increase of 6.67 centimeters, or a mean annual increase of .11 centimeters (Table 35).

Bolk and v. d. Broek [1] observed that increase was general but not uniform. Bolk noticed that in the same vicinity factory workers were taller than the farming classes, and that those in the northern provinces were taller than people in the south engaged in the same kinds of labor. He attributed the discrepancy to racial difference, believing that the Nordic provinces in the north showed more increase than the southern Alpine provinces.

For *Switzerland*, Hovelacque [2] has shown that the increase in stature of recruits in the canton of St. Marie Vesubie over a period of 160 years has been 9.5 centimeters (Table 36).

TABLE 36

MEAN STATURE OF SWISS RECRUITS (1792–1872)

Years	M
1792–99	155.50
1800–10	157.00
1811–20	159.00
1821–30	....
1831–40	159.70
1841–50	162.00
1851–60	163.00
1861–72	165.00

Increase 9.50   Annual increase .119

In *Italy* data are not complete, but show likewise considerable modification in stature. The results for three periods follow.

TABLE 37

STATURE OF ITALIANS (1855–96)

Years	M	Authority
1855–59	162.4	Lombroso * (Ref. Livi)
1867	163.4	Lombroso†
1896	164.5	Livi

* R. Livi, *Antropometria Militare* (1896), p. 32.
† C. Lombroso, *Sulla Statura degli Italiani*, Archivo per Antropologia e la Etnologia (1873).

[1] Martin (1928), pp. 263–264.   [2] Martin (1928), p. 264.

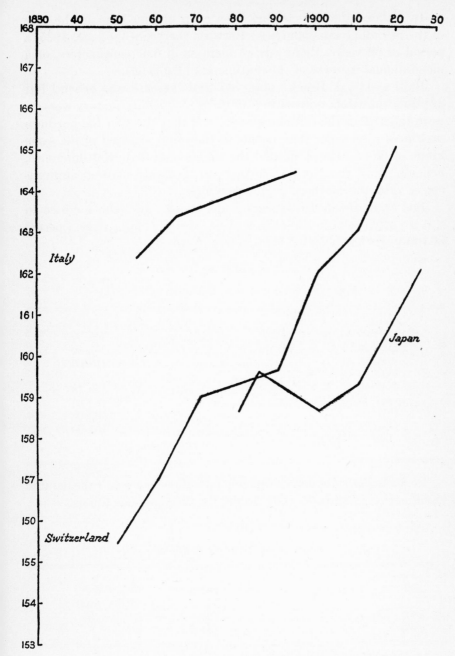

FIG. 3. Stature increases by decades for Italy, Switzerland, and Japan

[37]

Between 1855 and 1896, a period of 41 years, there is an increase of 2.1 centimeters, or an annual increase of .05 centimeters.

This figure we may consider as the general increase per annum of the Mediterranean area as confirmed by measurements from *Spain*. Oloriz [1] in 1896 gives the stature of conscripts from Andalusia (the mean of the eight provinces) as 164.6 centimeters. In 1930 the stature recorded by Hulse [2] was 166.5 centimeters. The difference of 1.9 centimeters would mean an annual increase of .056 centimeters. It becomes apparent, therefore, that the rate of increase is fairly uniform for the whole of Europe, although there is as yet only scanty data from which to draw any definite conclusions.

Were measurements restricted to Europe alone the results would seem to indicate some racial qualification or peculiarity, manifested in varying degrees according to comparative statures during a given period. The phenomenon appears not to be restricted to Europe alone, for it has been observed in Japan over a period of more than 50 years.

For *Japan*, Matsumura [3] has shown that the same tendency towards stature increase exists. In fact, the increase there is even more striking than in Europe or America. There is a difference in male students of 2.69 centimeters over a 10 year period and in female students of 1.06 centimeters, representing a mean annual increase of .27 centimeters for the males and .11 centimeters for the females. Matsumura's measurements show a mean of $161.98 \pm .05$ on 5970 males and $149.92 \pm .09$ on 1200 females. [4] The measurements represent the Empire proper as a whole with the exception of the Northern Island.

Matsumura accounts for the discrepancies between his measurements and those of former observers on the basis of the differences in periods. Tables 38, 39 are arranged from Matsumura according to dates of observations. No dates are given for the Nippon Life Insurance Company.

In the case of conscripts there is a shift in the mode from the 157.5 to the 160.5 categories over the period 1912–21 as calculated by Matsumura. The tables are given in percentages.

---

[1] D. F. Oloriz, *Discursos Leidos en la Real Academia De Medicina* (1896), p. 60.

[2] F. Hulse, Unpublished Data, Peabody Museum, Cambridge, Massachusetts (1930).

[3] A. Matsumura, *On the Cephalic Index and Stature of the Japanese and their Local Differences*, Journal Faculty of Science, Imperial University of Tokyo, Sec. V, Anthropology, vol. i, Part 1 (1925), pp. 79–87.

[4] Cf. Tables 119–120.

The figures of Matsumura are further supported by those of Yoshida,[1] who compares measurements on the inhabitants of Tokyo with those of previous authorities. The differences here, although not great, still show the general trend towards a greater stature (Table 38).

It would seem on the basis of these studies that the increase, as in the case of the Old American material, has become progressively more rapid within the past few decades.

TABLE 38

COMPARISON OF STATURES OF INHABITANTS OF TOKYO AT DIFFERENT TIMES

Years	No.	Age	M	Authority
1885	2500	20	158.50	Baelz
1901	254	20	159.10	Miwa
1926	6662	(Majority) 20	160.20	Yoshida
	Increase 1.70		Annual increase .041	

It is quite apparent that there has been a very marked increase in the stature of the Japanese, especially in the student classes of today.

The increases for the various countries considered are graphically illustrated in Figures 18 and 19. The peoples of North-European countries, including Norway, Sweden, Denmark, Holland, and Old Americans, are thrown together in Figure 19 and the mean of the total indicated.

There is rather steady increase up to about the years 1870–80. After a slight pause of about a decade there is a subsequent more pronounced increase. Between 1910 and 1920 there is a secondary falling off, which becomes more marked in the succeeding decade.

We may conclude, therefore, that for North Europeans and Old Americans there seems to have been a similar rate and variation in increase, with a slight drop about 1880 and again about 1920. At present the rate of annual increment is still on the decline.

For Central Europe the only information secured seems to show a more marked increase among the Alpines than was the case among the Nordics, but the material is considerably older for Switzerland and may not be comparable.

[1] Y. Yoshida, On the Development of Stature, Weight and Head Circumference of the Japanese, Journal Anthropological Society, Tokyo, vol. XLIII, No. 484 (February, 1928), pp. 75–76.

For Southern Europe the Italian and Spanish data are fairly consistent, and show less increase than in either Central or Northern Europe. In Japan the increase is almost as pronounced as in Central Europe.

TABLE 39

STATURE OF MALE JAPANESE * (1878–1925)

Years	No.	Age	M	Authority
		Various Groups (1878–1925)		
1878	12	...	156.90	Weisbach
1879	70	20–29	160.30	Ayrton
1883–88	28	...	155.50	Mugnier
1885	53 (students)	15–38	161.50	Baelz
1885	13 (workmen)	20–57	161.90	"
1889	15	...	157.80	Soller
1901	2142	20–40	158.62	Miwa
1910(?)	6066	...	159.16	Nippon Life Insurance Company
1925	5970	Adults	161.98	Matsumura

Students (1909–18)

Years	No.	M
1909	15,017	159.82
1910	15,482	160.20
1911	15,938	161.23
1912	15,911	161.80
1913	16,148	161.07
1914	16,007	161.20
1915	16,860	161.32
1916	16,052	161.47
1917	15,363	162.44
1918	14,910	162.50
Increase 2.69		Annual increase .268

* Modified from Matsumura.

Stature and Physique

Although of secondary consideration, the importance of stature in relation to various non-mensurable factors is not to be ignored, especially as they concern the student population of America. From time to time studies have been made on the relationship of stature to physique, ability, pigmentation, and numerous other factors which cannot be measured by the usual means of inches or pounds. The three factors mentioned are therefore discussed in their relationship to the student population.

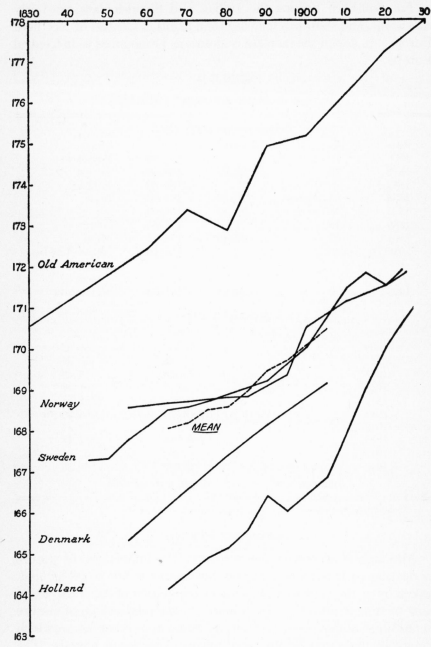

Fig. 4. Stature increases by decades for Europeans and Old Americans

It is a well-known fact that exercise has a very considerable influence upon stature and general body build. However, persons who are physically well endowed are more likely to indulge in strenuous exercise than those of less vigorous constitution. It consequently becomes difficult to determine whether people become taller because they exercise or exercise because they are tall. However that may be, there is always a selective factor operating, and this is especially true of such carefully chosen groups as college varsity teams as compared with the college as a whole.

In the different departments and among the athletes Sargent [1] found a number of differences. Table 40 shows the means of the athletic and non-athletic groups.

TABLE 40

STATURE AND WEIGHT OF ATHLETIC AND NON-ATHLETIC GROUPS — SARGENT

Group	No.	Period	Stature	Weight
University crew	240	1880–00	177.5	152.1
University football	295	1880–00	176.5	157.6
Lawrence Scientific School	505	1902–06	174.5	143.3
Academic Department	530	1904–06	174.5	140.0

Sargent suggests that two classes are developing, one scholastic and the other athletic, although his arguments are based solely on greater increases in the athletic groups than in the non-athletic and are hence hardly justifiable. The greater emphasis on athletics may be one of the contributive factors in the general increase of the population at large.

Stature and Ability

Although it is somewhat hazardous to base conclusions regarding ability on the basis of comparative stature, it must be remembered that the considerations are limited both racially and as regards age. Quite likely one of the chief factors to be held accountable for the negative correlation between height and age in student groups is that students who are physically fit are prepared earlier, and as a corollary it follows that those who enter late are in proportion to their age less developed than those who enter young. It has also been shown by Porter [2] in 1893 that the average height and weight

[1] 1908, pp. 248–256.   [2] Sargent (1908), pp. 248–256.

of those who were in the higher scholastic ratings were greater than those of students in the lower. "In other words, he found that pupils who were mentally the most precocious were also physically the most precocious." His conclusions have been confirmed by Hastings in Omaha, Byers in Cambridge, Christopher in Chicago, Roberts in London, Burgerstein in Vienna, and Leharzig in St. Petersburg.

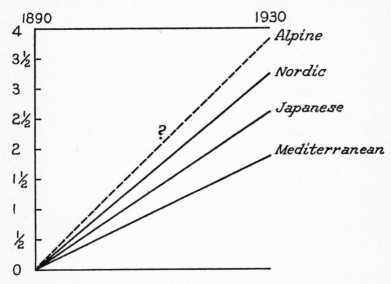

FIG. 5. Increase in stature in different peoples between 1890–1930

We may conclude, therefore, that increase in stature should be considered as a good sign, for students are getting both younger and physically more fit than those of a generation ago.

Stature and Pigmentation

From observations made on the soldiers of the Revolutionary War the relationship between complexion and stature shows that the darker complexioned people are somewhat taller. This is in accord with the findings of Baxter[1] on Civil War soldiers and Hrdlička[2] on Old Americans. Table 41 shows the relative heights in relation to complexion, the mean for lights being 171.85 and for darks 172.75. The difference (.90) is not significant, being only 1.98

[1] J. H. Baxter, *Statistics, Med. and Anth., of the Provost-Marshal General's Bureau,* i (1875), 24.
[2] 1925, p. 82.

in terms of the probable error, or less than twice the square root of the sum of the squares of the probable errors of the two means.

Data are unfortunately lacking for the student series. If we may assume that complexion has a high correlation with hair color, it would appear that here again the darker pigmented individuals, at least so far as the above-mentioned trait is concerned, tend also to be somewhat taller. The fathers are both shorter and lighter haired than the sons (cf. p. 61).

TABLE 41

STATURE IN LIGHT AND DARK COMPLEXIONED MEN

	Light Complexioned			Dark Complexioned		
	No.	M	p. e.	No.	M	p. e.
Revolutionary War soldiers	180	171.85	.33	135	172.75	.31
Old Americans:						
First series	25	172.8	...	25	173.1	...
Second series	25	174.1	...	25	174.2	...
United States	126,445	171.84	...	64,176	172.15	...
British America	9,506	170.61	...	4,859	170.37	...
England...............	6,804	169.12	...	2,845	169.22	...
Ireland...............	20,378	169.56	...	8,617	169.56	...
Germany	20,559	168.99	...	9,041	168.98	...

As to hair color, we have already observed that with an increase in stature the hair becomes darker. Eye color, on the contrary, seems to decrease in amount of pigmentation.

Weight

In weight the fathers in the small series averaged 140.24 pounds ±.55 and the sons 150.30 ±.53, a difference of 10.06 pounds, the fathers representing 93.31 percent of the sons' measurement. The difference is thus very significant, and as we shall presently see is only slightly less than in stature. For the large series for fathers and sons the difference is 8.15 pounds.[1]

Again the question arises as to the rate of increase, its tendencies, and whether there is any fluctuation in degree of correlation with

[1] In the large series the statistical constants for the two generations are:

	No.	M	p. e.	σ	p. e.	V	p. e.	Range
Sons	1461	149.48	.35	18.00	.25	12.04	.17	103–246
Fathers	1166	141.33	.35	17.70	.25	12.52	.18	95–218.5
Difference	8.15							

height increase. The fact that there is an increase in weight and height over a period of 35 years does not necessarily mean that the increase in one has been complementary to increase in the other. There is, however, as we shall presently discover, a certain degree of relationship existing between the two.

In order then first to clarify the question of rate of annual increase Table 42 has been prepared.

TABLE 42

WEIGHT OF MALE STUDENTS BY BIRTH DECADES — LARGE SERIES

Years	No.	M	p. e.	σ	p. e.	V	p. e.	Range
1836–45	2	140.00	8.35	17.50	5.90	12.50	4.21	125–160
1846–55	43	140.65	1.71	16.65	1.22	11.84	.86	115–175
1856–65	335	138.40	.60	16.25	.42	11.74	.31	95–205
1866–75	505	139.70	.49	16.20	.34	11.60	.24	95–205
1876–85	307	146.85	.73	18.75	.51	12.77	.35	100–220
1886–95	268	149.15	.72	17.50	.51	11.73	.34	110–210
1896–05	614	148.90	.49	18.25	.35	12.26	.23	105–230
1906–15	546	149.05	.49	16.71	.33	11.21	.22	105–250

When reduced to more comparable figures, with the differences calculated as in stature, the variations in amounts of annual increment by decades are quite marked. The succeeding tables will show how much more variable and irregular weight is than stature.

TABLE 43

INCREASE OF WEIGHT FOR MALE STUDENTS BY BIRTH DECADES — LARGE SERIES

Years	1856–65	1866–75	1876–85	1886–95	1896–00
1866–75	1.30	..			
1876–85	8.45	7.15	..		
1886–95	10.75	9.45	2.30	..	
1896–05	10.50	9.20	2.05	−.25	..
1906–15	10.65	9.35	2.20	−.10	.15
Annual increase	.13	.71	.23	−.02	.01
	Mean annual increase	.21			

The mean annual increase as calculated is .21 pounds or 2.10 pounds per decade. Since the mean decade increase is 2.59 times the probable error, it would take about 11.6 years for a significant difference to occur. This is less than for stature with a figure of

3.48 and a consequent significant difference every 8½ years. The results confirm our discoveries in the rest of the body measurements and correlations, in which it is quite apparent that the sons are on the whole slenderer than their fathers in proportion to their height.

A further fact of interest is that the annual increase in stature was greatest in 1860. In weight the peak was also reached in the same decade, but the falling off has been more marked in weight than in stature. At present there is only .01 pounds, or practically no annual increase, whereas in stature the rate is still about .07 centimeters per annum.

TABLE 44

DIFFERENCES OF WEIGHT IN TERMS OF PROBABLE ERROR FOR MALE STUDENTS BY BIRTH DECADES — LARGE SERIES

Years	1856–65	1866–75	1876–85	1886–95	1896–05
1866–75	1.69	..			
1876–85	8.96	8.14	..		
1886–95	11.46	10.84	2.25	..	
1896–05	13.56	13.28	2.34	−.29	..
1906–15	13.74	13.49	2.51	−.12	.22
Mean decade figure.................			2.59		

To summarize: (1) sons are absolutely both heavier and taller than their fathers; (2) male students as a whole have shown a mean annual increase of .21 pounds during the past 50 years; (3) weight increase has been to a certain extent associated with stature increase insofar as the greatest increases were noted in the same decade (1856–65), but the falling off of increment has been more marked for weight; (4) proportionally weight has not increased at the same rate as stature, consequently significant difference occurs every 11½ years as opposed to every 8½ in stature; (5) men are today getting taller and slenderer, even though in absolute weight they exceed their parents.

Sitting Height

The mean sitting height for the fathers is 90.95 centimeters, for the sons 92.14 centimeters, a difference of 1.19. In relative sitting heights [1] the fathers are in excess of the sons, the index for the former being 52.30 and for the latter 51.91. The excess in the sons is due to increased stature. By comparison with the increase in pubic height

[1] For list of indices, see Table 50.

(1.92 centimeters), it is quite apparent that the excess in total stature of sons over fathers is due to greater increase in the lower limb than in the trunk. The further significances are discussed in connection with indices.

Knee Height and Pubic Height

The mean knee height in the fathers (46.66 centimeters) is .36 below that of the sons with a mean of 47.02. This again is very near the figure for Old Americans at large. When subtracted from the pubic height (fathers 87.10, sons 89.02 centimeters) the approximate thigh lengths are respectively 40.44 and 42.00, with an increase in the sons of 1.56 in the upper segment of the leg. In summary, then, the difference over one generation in knee height is .36, in upper leg length 1.56, a total of 1.92 or 54 percent of the total height increase of 3.55. The region of greatest stature increase is, therefore, in the lower limb.

Navel Height and Sternal Height

In navel height the actual difference between fathers and sons is 3.30. Since we have discovered that 54 percent of the total stature increase has been in the upper leg region and the total stature increase is only 3.55, the only explanation for the marked excess in navel height is that its proportional position has been changed. It has evidently moved upwards on the body. The means for navel height in fathers and sons are respectively 103.72 and 107.02 centimeters.

In sternal height the difference is 3.27, slightly less than in navel height. This is more in accord with expectations, for it represents 92 percent of the total increase.

Span

Span increase has exceeded that of stature. The means for the fathers and sons, 178.20 and 181.98 centimeters respectively, leave a balance of 3.78 in favor of the sons. The indices for the two generations are consequently slightly different, being in the fathers 102.30 and in the sons 102.52.

Foot Length

Foot length has not increased as much as other measurements. The mean in the fathers is 25.98 and in the sons 26.15 centimeters. The difference of .17 accounts for the difference in relative foot lengths of 14.93 and 14.73. The proportional increase is .65 percent.

Arm Length

In total arm length the increase is only .26, as opposed to 1.92 in pubic height or approximate leg length. Peculiarly enough, in the case of arm length there is a slight decrease in the upper arm length and consequently the increase has all taken place in the lower segment. In actual measurements the mean for the upper arm in the fathers is 37.55 and in the sons 36.80 centimeters, a decrease of .75. The lower arm means are correspondingly 46.92 and 47.93, an increase of 1.01. The net increase is therefore not proportionally distributed between the two segments. In total arm length the mean for the fathers is 84.47 and for the sons 84.73 centimeters.

To summarize, increase in arm length is only 14 percent of the increase in leg length. Relatively, however, the increase is more nearly the same. Further, the increment is not proportionally distributed, the upper segment having absolutely slightly decreased, whereas the lower arm has increased more than enough to compensate for the foreshortening of the upper segment. Proximal increase in the legs is reversed to distal increase in the arms.

Length and Breadth of Head

Head length was measured on sons only. The mean is 194.13 millimeters. Head breadth is 150.90 millimeters and the cephalic index 78. Head breadth in the fathers is 153.00 millimeters, 2.1 millimeters greater than in the sons. Since increase in stature is fairly highly correlated with increase in head length, we should expect a decrease in head breadth on the part of the sons. If we were to assume a head length of 192.50 for the fathers we should have a cephalic index of 78.4. The latter figure is merely an approximation, and is only surmised on the basis of comparative statures. Both figures would compare favorably with other Old American material. (Cf. cephalic index in *Brothers*, p. 73.)

Girth Measurements

In girth measurements increases are most marked. Chest girths show increments of 4.00 centimeters for normal position and 2.50 for full expansion. The chest expansion from resting position (not completely exhaled) to fully expanded in the fathers is 5.00 and in the sons 3.50, although in actual girths the sons exceed the fathers by 4.00 in normal and 2.50 in expanded measurements. The normal means are respectively 86.88 and 90.88, and means expanded 91.88 and 94.38 centimeters.

In other girth measurements the greatest increases are in hips, thigh, knee, upper arm, forearm, and neck. Lesser increments are noted in waist, calf, elbow, and waist. The increases have been greatest, therefore, in the upper extremities of the limbs and least in the lower. In the trunk the lower regions have shown greater increase than the thoracic.

Breadth Measurements

Peculiarly enough, in breadth of hips there has been a decrease of .14 centimeters, whereas in girth of hips there has been an increase of 2.56. The same phenomenon occurred among the women, in whom the breadth decreased by 2.73 and the girth increased by 1.09. In other measurements increases have ranged from .08 in breadth between nipples to .99 in shoulder breadths.

Summary of Thirty Measurements

The distribution of stature increase in various parts of the body are graphically illustrated in Figures 6 and 7. Figure 6 represents the various proportions of the sons (unbroken) superimposed on those of the fathers (broken). The various relationships above described will be apparent. In Figure 7 the increase in stature is divided by centimeters and by percentages, accounting thus for the total of 3.55 centimeters.

In all measurements with the exceptions of head breadth, breadth of hips, and length of upper arm there have been increases of varying amounts during the past generation. These increases have been both absolutely and proportionally greatest in heights and lengths, girths and breadths, respectively. The most notable features about changes in physical measurements are:

(1) Increase in stature of $3\frac{1}{2}$ centimeters and in weight of over 10 pounds.

(2) Greater increase in leg length than trunk length.

(3) In leg length greater increase in the upper segment, the reverse holding for the arm; in trunk length greatest increase in the lower sections.

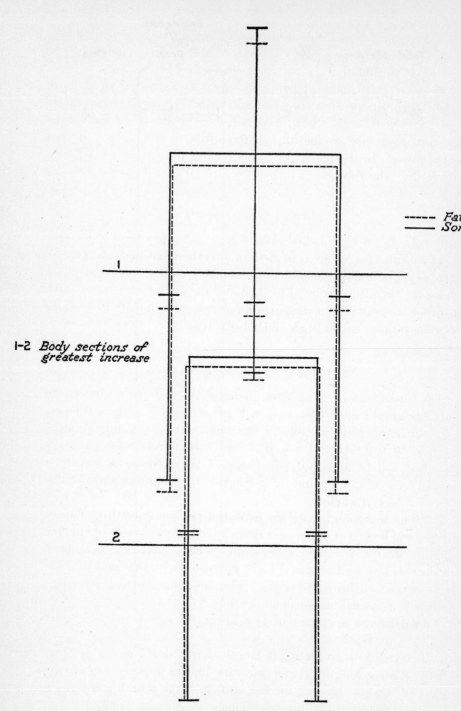

----- Father
―――― Sons

1-2 *Body sections of greatest increase*

FIG. 6. Increases of various body parts of sons over fathers

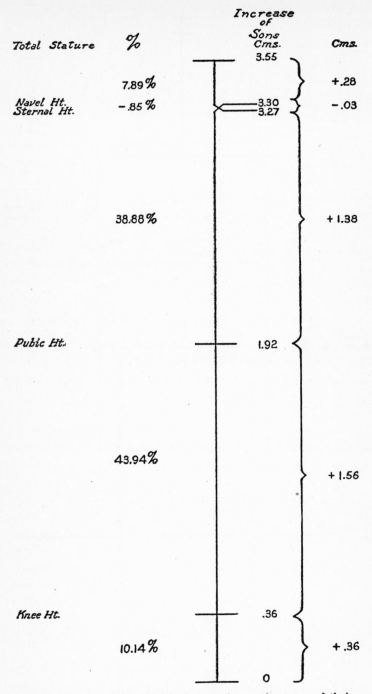

FIG. 7. Increases of various body parts by centimeters and their proportion to total stature increase

(4) The greatest increase in the middle of the body, including the lower segments of the upper limbs, the upper segments of the lower limbs, and the lower part of the trunk, with lesser increases in the leg and least above the sternum.

(5) Increase in hip girth accompanied by decrease in breadth.

(6) Greater girth increases in upper sections of the extremities and the trunk than in the lower.

(7) Decrease in head breadth with increase in stature — an expected phenomenon.

The regions indicated as those of greatest increase are the same as the regions where increase takes place in normal individual growth. We may assume, therefore, that whenever increase takes place from one generation to another it is likely to occur in the regions where increase occurs in the normal individual, and, further, that the rate of increase will be approximately proportional.

UNIT INCREASES OF MEASUREMENTS AND PERCENTILE RELATIONS

In Table 45 the various unit differences and percentile proportions are listed for comparison.

When grouping is done by types of measurements some interesting facts are revealed. In weight, as expected, the percentage is quite low (93.31). In heights and lengths the percentage is 98.57, or only slightly above that of stature. In girths the figure is comparatively high, but is not especially noteworthy. The amount for breadths is liable to give a false impression. The reason for the high percentage (99.15) is due to the great variety. In some instances the means are greater in the fathers and in others in the sons. Thus, while the mean percentage is very nearly the same, in shoulder breadth and other important measurements the sons are broader than the fathers, and hence have low coefficients of correlation due to greater variability; in breadth of hips the reverse is true. The percentages must therefore be compared with the coefficients of correlation and the statistical constants of the seriations in order to understand the apparently conflicting data.

The total mean 98 percent conforms to that of stature and we may generalize broadly, therefore, that in men the percentage of all measurements, the average proportional amount of increase of sons' over fathers' measurements, would likely be in the neighborhood of 2 percent.

TABLE 45

UNIT DIFFERENCES AND PERCENTILE RELATIONS BETWEEN FATHERS AND
SONS — SMALL SERIES

	Difference	Percent (100 = Sons)
Weight......................	10.06	93.31
Stature	3.55	98.00
Sitting height	1.19	98.71
Knee height	.36	99.23
Pubic height	1.92	97.84
Navel height.................	3.30	96.92
Sternal height...............	3.27	97.75
Girth of neck	.94	97.36
Girth of chest (N)	4.00	95.60
Girth of chest (F)	2.50	97.35
Girth of waist...............	.60	99.18
Girth of hips................	2.56	97.21
Girth of thigh...............	1.82	96.63
Girth of knee	1.10	97.00
Girth of calf	.50	98.60
Girth of upper arm	1.41	95.42
Girth of elbow	.29	98.86
Girth of forearm	1.02	96.19
Girth of wrist	.19	98.84
Breadth of head	−2.10*	101.39
Breadth of neck	.23	97.94
Breadth of shoulders	.99	97.73
Breadth of waist	.57	97.80
Breadth of hips	−.14	100.43
Breadth between nipples	.08	99.61
Shoulder-elbow length	−.75	102.04
Elbow-finger length	1.01	97.89
Length of foot	.17	99.35
Span........................	3.78	97.92

* Millimeters.

TABLE 46

UNIT DIFFERENCES AND PERCENTILE RELATIONS OF GROUPED MEASUREMENTS
BETWEEN FATHERS AND SONS — SMALL SERIES *

	Difference	Percent (100 = Sons)
Weight......................	10.06	93.31
Heights and lengths	1.78	98.57
Girths	1.41	97.35
Breadths	−.62	99.15
Total mean		98.00

* See Table 47 for large series.

For the large series the figures of Table 47, which includes only the measurements of stature and weight, check closely with those of the smaller group.

TABLE 47

UNIT DIFFERENCES OF WEIGHT AND STATURE AND PERCENTILE RELATIONS BETWEEN FATHERS AND SONS — LARGE SERIES

	Difference	Percent (100 = Sons)
Weight......................	8.15	94.54
Stature	3.39	98.08

COEFFICIENTS OF CORRELATION

The coefficients of correlation between fathers and sons are in most instances much lower than would normally be expected. In no

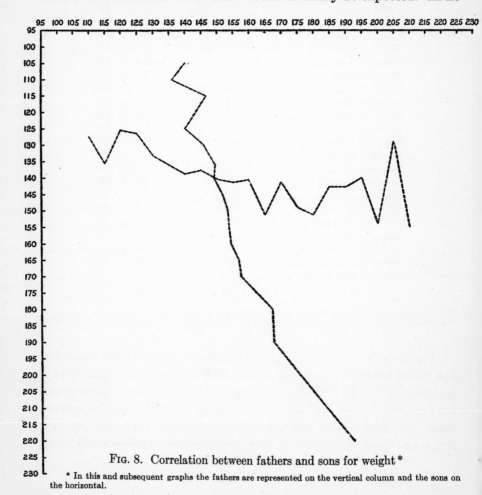

FIG. 8. Correlation between fathers and sons for weight *

* In this and subsequent graphs the fathers are represented on the vertical column and the sons on the horizontal.

case is the resemblance over .40 (Table 48), and in most measurements it is in the twenties and thirties.

TABLE 48

Coefficients of Correlation between Fathers and Sons for Various Measurements — Small Series

	No.	r	p. e.
Weight................	478	.29	.03
Stature	479	.38	.03
Sitting height	409	.37	.03
Knee height	476	.36	.03
Pubic height	476	.36	.03
Navel height.............	477	.32	.03
Sternal height............	478	.40	.03
Girth of head	477	.23	.03
Girth of neck	478	.22	.03
Girth of chest (N)	479	.26	.03
Girth of chest (F)	477	.23	.03
Girth of waist.............	478	.16	.03
Girth of hips..............	476	.26	.03
Girth of thigh.............	478	.26	.03
Girth of knee	478	.22	.03
Girth of calf	479	.29	.03
Girth of upper arm	479	.13	.03
Girth of elbow	472	.23	.03
Girth of forearm	479	.22	.03
Girth of wrist	479	.37	.03
Breadth of head	474	.12	.03
Breadth of neck	477	.16	.03
Breadth of shoulders	476	.18	.03
Breadth of waist	478	.15	.03
Breadth of hips	479	.21	.03
Breadth between nipples ...	476	.18	.03
Shoulder-elbow length	477	.19	.03
Elbow-finger length	474	.33	.03
Length of foot	477	.37	.03
Span....................	474	.34	.03

The series is numerically sufficient, the frequencies for the different measurements averaging about 475 couples. A comparison of the frequencies with those of the seriations will show a discrepancy between the totals for the fathers and the couples in the correlations. In order not to lose the value of second, third, and succeeding sons, these were paired with the fathers independently, with the consequence that the fathers in about 75 instances have been duplicated.

In stature the coefficient is .38, and it is to be expected that stature should conform more closely than weight in parental inheritance, since weight is more variable than stature.

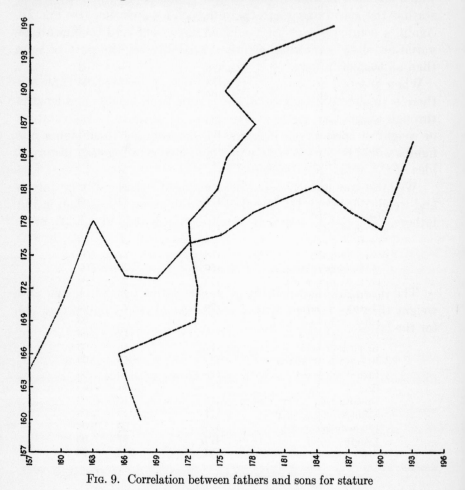

Fig. 9. Correlation between fathers and sons for stature

Sitting height, knee height, pubic height, navel height, sternal height, girth of wrist, elbow-fingertip length, length of foot, and span are all correlated with coefficients of over .30. All of the remaining coefficients fall below that figure, reaching as low as .12 in breadth of head. In Figures 8 and 9 weight of fathers and sons and stature of fathers and sons are plotted against each other.

More important, however, appear the actual differences in the means as indicated by the seriation comparisons. There is a difference in stature between fathers and sons of 3.55 centimeters. It is quite clear, therefore, that it is this great difference in actual bulk which has such an influence on results. Compared by percentages of stature the sons further substantiate such a conclusion (*see* Fig. 7). Again, a comparison of the standard deviations and coefficients of variation show somewhat greater variability on the part of sons than on that of fathers.

When grouped according to types of measurements (*see* Table 89) there is progressive decrease in correlation from heights and lengths through weight and girths to breadths. If we were to take stature or weight or span as our criterion for determining resemblance our figures would be far too high, and would give an altogether distorted idea of the actual relationships.

We must conclude that sons have changed considerably in stature and weight, although the variability in the group is less than in the fathers. The mean coefficient of correlation is only about .25, or $\frac{1}{4}$.

Cross-correlations of Fathers and Sons Separately

The sons show considerably more correlation between height and weight than the fathers, with a coefficient of .49 as opposed to .44 for the latter.

TABLE 49

COEFFICIENTS OF CORRELATION OF STATURE AND WEIGHT OF FATHERS AND SONS CROSS-CORRELATED — SMALL SERIES

	No.	r	p. e.
Fathers	397	.44	.03
Sons	480	.49	.02

The figures are slightly lower than Castle[1] found on 1000 Harvard men (.544), but are very close to Pearson's results on Cambridge men with a coefficient of .486. The mean of the present series is .465 for 877 men. Graphically the two correlations are illustrated in Figures 10 and 11.

[1] W. E. Castle, *Genetics and Eugenics* (1926), p. 97.

We may conclude, therefore, that so far as relationship between height and weight are concerned there is even closer affiliation now than in the past generation. In general the coefficient would be

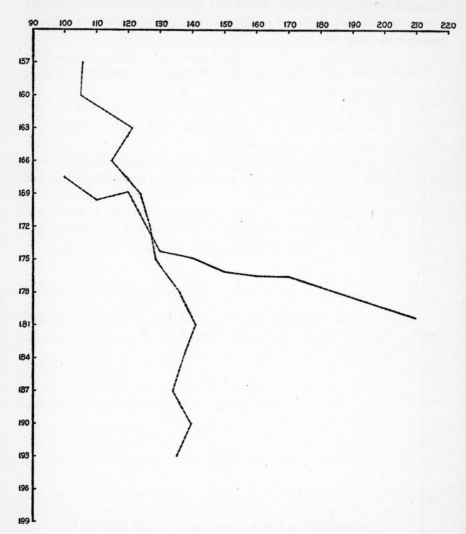

FIG. 10. Correlation between stature and weight for fathers

about .5, or ½. In the case of the women, to be noted later, the coefficient is .45 for the daughters while for the mothers it is .51. The mean .455 is practically identical with that for men.

INDICES

The various measurements in proportion to stature of fathers and sons are given in Table 50. In 11 out of 18 indices the sons exceed the fathers. Cephalic index is discussed under head length and head breadth on page 48.

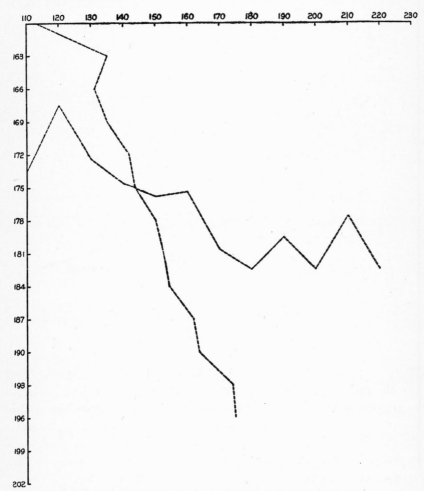

FIG. 11. Correlation between stature and weight for sons

In relative sitting height the sons have a somewhat smaller index showing that increase in stature is due to an increase in leg length rather than in trunk length. In absolute measurements the increase has been about 2 centimeters in the former and 1½ in the latter. It would seem, further, that the leg increase has been greatest in the upper segment, as above noted. In arm length, however, increase has been greatest in the lower segment. It appears, therefore, that where there is increase in stature it is greatest in the thigh, slightly less in the trunk, and less in the leg. The fact also that in the sons the

TABLE 50

VARIOUS MEASUREMENTS OF FATHERS AND SONS IN PROPORTION TO
STATURE — SMALL SERIES

	Fathers	Sons
Span	102.30	102.52
Sitting height	52.30	51.91
Navel height	59.63	60.29
Pubic height	50.00	50.15
Sternal height	81.51	81.75
Trunk	31.45	31.59
Upper arm	21.58	20.73
Lower arm	26.97	27.00
Knee height	26.82	26.49
Foot length	14.93	14.73
Breadth between nipples	11.64	11.46
Breadth of hips	19.00	18.55
Breadth of shoulders	24.53	24.61
Girth of chest	49.93	51.20
Girth of thigh	29.95	30.39
Girth of waist	41.89	41.40
Girth of hips	51.31	51.74
Knee height-pubic height	23.24	23.81

difference in indices between navel height and pubic height is less than the difference between navel height and sternal height and that the reverse is true in the fathers, indicates that greatest increase in trunk length has occurred above the navel in the sons, although the relative navel height in the latter is in excess of the fathers'. In conclusion we may summarize the regions of increase in order of importance as follows: (1) thigh, (2) lower trunk, (3) leg, (4) above the sternum.

OBSERVATIONS

The only observations for which there are data on students are hair color and eye color. Probably no observations are more difficult to record nor so liable to misrepresentation and misinterpretation. It should be made clear in advance, therefore, that whatever conclusions have been drawn are only of the most general nature and are compiled from observations of various recorders, each with his own technique. The factors of personal equation and method are consequently of greatest importance and considerably lessen the value of the results.

Besides the data on students there is additional information for eye color of Revolutionary War soldiers and for complexions of Revolutionary War soldiers and sailors of the Peabody Ships.

Hair Color

The mean square contingency coefficient for hair color between fathers and sons is .30 for a sample of 438 individuals. It would appear from the percentages in Table 51 that hair color is getting darker. Hrdlička [1] has shown that there is a tendency for hair color

TABLE 51

COEFFICIENT OF MEAN SQUARE CONTINGENCY FOR HAIR COLOR OF FATHERS AND SONS — SMALL SERIES

	Fathers		Sons	
	No.	Percent	No.	Percent
Very light	5	1.14	4	.91
Light brown	149	34.02	18	4.11
Medium brown	135	30.83	317	72.38
Dark brown	122	27.85	21	4.79
Black	21	4.79	64	14.61
Red	6	1.37	14	3.20
	438	100.00	438	100.00

C .30

to darken, and has correlated the increase in stature and the intensification of pigment. Since there has been more increase in stature on the part of Old Americans, it would logically follow that eye color should darken appreciably more than among Englishmen. There is an increase in the percentage of red-haired individuals from 1.37 percent to 3.20 percent, a considerable change, although the true value of the information is open to some doubt. Only those recorded as red were so considered, and doubtless many were discarded who might in the succeeding generation have been so classified had the same method of recording been employed. In very light hair there

[1] 1925, p. 82.

was a slight but significant drop. Probably the most important difference was the increase by 10 percent in the black-haired group, which largely affects the value of the contingency coefficient.

In comparison with other Old American data, the terminology employed in originally designating the different types of hair makes it impossible to compare favorably the present series with those of previous investigators. For comparison with European material also, the methods of recording are so different and the technique of determining pigment so varied that it is possible to make only the most imperfect and rough generalizations. The data on Revolutionary War soldiers measured in 1775 show that hair color at that time was considerably lighter than now. The majority percentage is in the first two categories as shown in Table 52.

By combining or lumping the different groups given by Hrdlička [1] and comparing them with the present series we have the results given in Table 52.

TABLE 52

COMPARISONS OF HAIR COLOR

	Old Americans, Hrdlička (1000)	Old Americans, Present Series (438)		Revolutionary War Soldiers (314)	Present England and Scotland (14,557)
		Fathers	Sons		
Light proper and light brown	21.30	35.16	5.02	44.27	16.70
Medium and dark ...	75.00	58.68	77.17	39.49	73.10
Black	1.10	4.79	14.61	13.06	5.80
Red	2.60	1.37	3.20	1.91	4.40
Gray				1.27	

It appears, therefore, that the Old Americans in the present series, both fathers and sons, are considerably different from either of the comparative series. It would seem that a fair percentage of the sons in the medium or dark group should belong in the light group, and the reverse might hold in the case of the fathers. However that may be, it is quite clear that there is a significant difference at least between the fathers and the sons, the latter showing an obvious tendency toward the deeper shades. The Revolutionary War soldiers show by far the greatest percentage of lights and light browns, but it is more than likely that the high figures are due to inaccurate observation.

[1] 1925, p. 51, modified from Table 25.

TABLE 53

HAIR COLOR OF REVOLUTIONARY WAR SOLDIERS *

	N	Percent
Light	132	42.04
Fair	7	2.23
Brown	32	10.19
Dark	92	29.30
Black	41	13.06
Red	6	1.91
Gray	4	1.27
	314	100.00

* Material calculated from records in the Rolls of the Soldiers in the Revolutionary War, New Hampshire State Papers, vol. II, Concord, New Hampshire.

The category designated as "fair" may for all practical purposes be included with the light.

We may summarize the subject of hair color as follows: (1) hair color has become considerably darker in the course of the past generation. There has been a noticeable increase in the dark brown, black, and red categories. (2) This is concurrent with an increase in stature but, as we shall presently see, a lessening of eye pigmentation. (3) The older generation appears to be noticeably lighter than the subjects of previous investigations on Old Americans and on present-day Scotch and English, but in the younger generation the condition is reversed. (4) The major color of the present younger generation is between medium and dark brown.

Eye Color

For eye color there is a slightly higher coefficient of mean square contingency of .40. This approaches more closely the figure given by Pearson [1] in his work on English fathers and sons, for whom he found a coefficient of correlation of .495 on 4000 pairs. Table 54 gives the various percentages of eye color for fathers and sons. In every category without exception, the line being drawn between the green-browns and the browns, the sons show a decrease in eye pigment from their fathers. In the three lighter categories the sons are in considerable excess of their fathers, whereas in the three darker groups the figures show the fathers are in proportion more numerous. There appears, therefore, to be no special connection between hair color and eye color as regards their heritable qualities.

[1] K. Pearson and A. Lee, *On the Laws of Inheritance in Man*, Biometrika, II (1903), 379.

TABLE 54

COEFFICIENT OF MEAN SQUARE CONTINGENCY FOR EYE COLOR OF FATHERS
AND SONS — SMALL SERIES

	Fathers		Sons	
	No.	Percent	No.	Percent
Blue	169	39.21	200	46.40
Gray	60	13.92	91	21.11
Green-brown..........	4	.93	15	3.48
Brown	129	29.93	111	25.75
Dark brown	55	12.76	6	1.40
Black	14	3.25	8	1.86
	431	100.00	431	100.00

C .40

The results are in conflict with those obtained by Hrdlička,[1] who
has found with an increase in stature complementary increases in
both hair and eye pigmentation, and we must assume that the great
difference is due to errors in observation in the present series.
It would seem hardly probable that hair color would change so
radically in one direction while eye color would act in exactly the
opposite way. It is not likely that such a high negative correlation
would normally exist.

For the Revolutionary War soldiers the following table shows that
there is again a predominance of the lighter colors, the majority
falling in the first two categories.

TABLE 55

EYE COLOR OF REVOLUTIONARY WAR SOLDIERS

	No.	Percent
Blue	78	25.00
Light	86	27.56
Gray	42	13.46
Dark	51	16.35
Black	55	17.63
	312	100.00

[1] 1925, p. 82, Tables 43 and 44.

By grouping various categories we get the following comparisons:

TABLE 56

COMPARATIVE EYE COLOR

	Fathers	Sons	Soldiers
Blue and light ..	39.21	46.40	52.56
Gray	13.92	21.11	13.46
Mixed	43.62	30.63	16.35
Black	3.25	1.86	17.63

There seems to be too large a percentage of blues and lights in all groups. It is more than likely that a fair percentage of individuals included in the first category should be placed in one or the other of the two succeeding classifications.

The results are so unsatisfactory that it is virtually impossible to compare the data with those of previous investigators. It is possible to get only a general impression. All of the present series appear to be considerably lighter than Hrdlička's material and the comparative data given by him for England, Wales, and Scotland.

Complexion

The material on complexion is limited to the data on sailors of the Peabody Ships and soldiers of the Revolutionary War. Contrary to general supposition, the seamen are much lighter complexioned than the soldiers. The ratio of light complexions to dark in the case of the former is roughly 10 to 15, in the case of the latter 7 to 5 (Table 57).

TABLE 57

COMPLEXIONS OF PEABODY SHIPS SEAMEN

	No.	Percent
Light	148	66.08
Dark	76	33.92
	224	100.00

The only apparent explanation would be to assume that there is no occupational difference and that difference in stature is to be held accountable for the discrepancy, for it has already been noted that correlated with an increase in stature is an increase in general pig-mentation. Tables 57 and 58 give the various percentages of light and dark complexions for the two groups.

TABLE 58

COMPLEXIONS OF REVOLUTIONARY WAR SOLDIERS

	No.	Percent
Light	180	56.96
Dark	136	43.04
	316	100.00

Comparative data from Baxter [1] show identical proportions in the division termed "British America" with the percentages for the sailors, the figures for light and dark complexioned men being respectively 66.18 and 33.82, or 10 to 5. For the United States at large Baxter gives the ratio also at about 10 to 5. For Europe the ratios are much higher, running in the case of England about 12½ to 5, and in those of Ireland and Germany 12 to 5. The per-centages are given in the table below.

TABLE 59

COMPARISONS OF COMPLEXIONS

	Light	Dark
Sailors	66.08	33.92
Soldiers	56.96	43.04
British America	66.18	33.82
United States	66.46	33.54
England	70.52	29.48
Ireland	80.28	19.72
Germany	69.46	30.54

It appears, therefore, that the sailors resemble most closely the British Americans, whereas the soldiers are much darker than any of the other groups listed. They approach more closely the Southern European material, if we may rely on the accuracy of the data.

[1] 1875, p. 24.

Summary of Observations

In hair color the sons are getting darker, as might be expected with an increase in stature. In eye color there is a lessening of pigmentation which can hardly be explained logically and is probably due to faulty methods of observation, for there is generally a fairly high correlation between hair color and eye color where racial factors are constant.

GRANDFATHERS AND GREAT-GRANDFATHERS

All of the information on the third and fourth ascending generations is derived from the questionnaires sent to the fathers of the small series. Three hundred odd letters were sent to the living fathers. Replies were received from over two hundred men, but in many cases information was lacking. It should be borne in mind that the figures for the grandfathers and great-grandfathers are based on the individual judgement of the person submitting the measurements, and are in no wise to be considered as accurate, but rather as approximate, estimates. Accurate measurements were returned for 13 men, a number inadequate for separate treatment. Measurements and comparisons are limited to stature and weight.

AGE

In stature and weight, although there are negative correlations for the student groups in both measurements, this holds true only for the few years of college life. After college, or at least after the twenty-fifth year, there is the usual increase with age until about the twenty-eighth year, and subsequent shrinkage at the rate of about one centimeter per decade. In weight the differences are even

TABLE 60

AGES AND FREQUENCIES OF FOUR GENERATIONS OF MALE STUDENTS AT TIMES OF MEASUREMENT

	No.	M
Great-grandfathers	8	50.
Grandfathers	92	30.
Fathers	132	19.
Sons	153	18.

more pronounced. There is greater increase with each successive year after maximum height is reached until after the sixtieth year. In Table 60 are given the frequencies and age means for the four generations compared. The fact that great-grandfathers were 50 when measured and the grandfathers 30 doubtless accounts for the marked difference between the weights of the two oldest generations as compared with the fathers or sons.

STATURE AND WEIGHT

In stature the increase from oldest to youngest generations is progressive. Some allowance should be made for the stature of the grandfathers, probably nearly a centimeter; for their fathers, a shrinkage allowance of approximately two centimeters from the maximum or one centimeter from the two youngest generations. In other words, the great-grandfathers will have first gained about one centimeter and subsequently lost about two. If corrections for age were introduced the figures for the four generations from oldest to youngest would probably be about 171.11, 173.13, 175.30, and 177.94. The progression is seen, therefore, to be both marked and regular. Allowing then 35 years for each generation, or a total of 105 years between the first and the fourth, the annual increase on

TABLE 61

STATURE OF MALE STUDENTS BY GENERATION GROUPS

	No.	M	p. e.	σ	p. e.	V	p. e.
Great-grandfathers	8	170.11	.87	3.66	.62	2.15	.36
Grandfathers	132	174.13	.44	7.41	.31	4.26	.18
Fathers	132	175.30	.36	6.12	.26	3.49	.15
Sons	153	177.94	.33	5.91	.23	3.32	.13

TABLE 62

WEIGHT OF MALE STUDENTS BY GENERATION GROUPS

	No.	M	p. e.	σ	p. e.	V	p. e.
Great-grandfathers	5	149.50	3.38	11.20	2.39	7.49	1.60
Grandfathers	125	152.35	1.62	26.95	1.16	17.69	.76
Fathers	125	145.75	1.23	20.45	.88	14.03	.60
Sons	141	151.10	1.09	18.45	.74	12.21	.49

the corrected basis would be .065 centimeters, slightly under the figure determined for the general increase of students as a whole for the past 80 years. Not corrected, the difference would probably run slightly higher, but not significantly.

Comparisons of Height and Weight at the Same Age

Far more convincing than the approximate measurements of the older generations contrasted with the younger are the answers to the question concerning the relative height and weight of the grand-fathers at the age of 19 in relation to those of the fathers. As shown in Table 63, approximately 19 percent of the fathers' measurements were less than the grandfathers' in stature, weight, or both; 20 percent were equal or balanced, i. e. if one was greater the other was less; and 60 percent, or nearly two-thirds, were greater in both measurements.

TABLE 63

Comparison of Fathers' and Grandfathers' Weights and Statures at the Age of Nineteen

	No.	Percent
Fathers' measurements less in one or both measurements	25	18.9
Fathers' and grandfathers' measurements equal or balanced	27	20.4
Fathers' measurements both greater	80	60.6
	132	99.9

It is apparent, therefore, that the grandfathers were definitely smaller on the average than the fathers at the age of 19, the age of measurement of the fathers.

Summary of Stature and Weight

The data on the third and fourth generations confirm the previous results obtained on the comparison between fathers and sons, at least as regards stature and weight. Between each generation there has been successive increase in both measurements. Weight is more variable than stature, and is consequently much more liable to change the value of the data, especially where age differences are great.

Random Samples of Stature Inheritance

The following examples are appended as illustrations. They were picked at random from the various groups and represent actual measurements made on individuals of one family, in one case over four generations. In all but one instance there appears to be fairly regular progressive increase.

TABLE 64

EXAMPLES OF THIRD AND FOURTH GENERATION STATURES OF FAMILIES
PICKED AT RANDOM

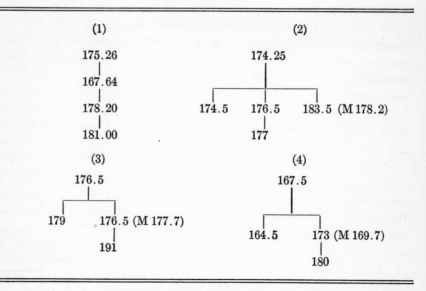

BROTHERS

It is a general belief, supported by very meagre scientific data, that older brothers are both taller and heavier than younger brothers and show proportional differences in other measurements. The truth of such a supposition has not, however, yet been proven. In fact, we shall have occasion to see that this is only partially correct, and can apply only to brothers up to the sixteenth year.

It is not the purpose of the present study to refute the work of previous investigators, but to add to the all too scanty material in a most interesting field of investigation and to clear up some questions which have hitherto remained obscure.

Age

Probably the greatest difficulty in making comparisons between fraternal siblings lies in the fact that generally no allowance is made for the difference in age. Thus, for example, Pearson [1] lumps his older and his younger brothers and sisters, irrespective of ages, and also disregards the fact that they were measured over a period of several years — both of which factors influence the measurements, as we shall have occasion to see. Boas,[2] again, although he is careful to differentiate age groups, fails to take into consideration the annual increase of the entire population, which radically influences the various measurements.

It is true, however, that age and bodily measurements (with the exception of weight in student classes) show either very slightly positive or even negative correlation, so that, except in cases where subadults of 15 or 16 are compared with adults of 25 to 28, there would probably not be any appreciable difference.

The material on which the present study is based was secured from both the large and the small men's series. The former yielded 251 first-born, 251 second-born, 33 third-born, 5 fourth-born, and 1 fifth-born, a total of 541 brothers. The latter furnished 79 couples (oldest and younger brothers). No account, of course, is taken of the sisters, or of other brothers who may have died in infancy. Hence the orders and numbers are limited to brothers living who have attended college and whose measurements are available and do not include the entire number of children in the family. In the case of the large series the comparisons are limited to stature and weight alone, whereas in the small series the comparisons are made between all the measurements included in the section dealing with fathers and sons, with cephalic index in addition.

It will be seen that in a few instances the measurements of more than two brothers were available. In order not to lose the value of the third, fourth, and fifth brothers in working out the various correlations the same plan was adopted as in the case of the fathers and sons, i. e. the oldest brother was correlated with the second, the third, the fourth, etcetera, independently, and was therefore repeated several times. Any differences in results would, however, be negligible, inasmuch as the dual relationships represent a total of

---

[1] K. Pearson and A. Lee (1903), pp. 444–446.
[2] F. Boas, *Growth of First-born Children*, Science, N. S., vol. I, no. 15 (1895), p. 402.

nearly 85 percent of the various couples used. The ages for the first-born, second-born, and third-born brothers for the large series are in all cases 18.2 years, or for general comparative purposes 18 years. The fourth and fifth brothers are too insignificant in numbers for comparison.

COMPARISON OF STATISTICAL CONSTANTS OF THIRTY MEASUREMENTS

In the small series, in every single measurement except breadth of head and breadth of waist there is an increase on the part of the younger brothers over the oldest. Although the number measured

TABLE 65

VARIOUS MEASUREMENTS OF OLDER BROTHERS — SMALL SERIES

	No.	M	p.e.	σ	p.e.	V	p.e.	Range
Weight..........	79	148.20	1.11	14.60	.79	9.85	.53	121–190
Stature	79	176.82	.44	5.85	.32	3.31	.18	161–187
Sitting height	79	91.60	.28	3.62	.20	3.95	.21	83–100
Navel height......	78	106.94	.37	4.28	.26	4.51	.24	95–118
Pubic height	78	88.84	.32	4.22	.23	4.75	.26	79–100
Sternal height.....	78	144.84	.41	5.40	.29	3.73	.20	131–154
Knee height	78	46.74	.19	2.46	.13	5.26	.28	41– 52
Girth of waist.....	79	73.30	.31	4.10	.22	5.59	.30	65– 82
Girth of hips......	79	91.14	.29	3.78	.20	4.15	.22	83–100
Girth of chest (N)	78	89.62	.38	5.02	.27	5.60	.30	79–102
Girth of chest (F) .	79	94.48	.35	4.58	.25	4.85	.26	85–106
Girth of head	79	56.98	.12	1.60	.09	2.81	.15	54– 60
Girth of neck	79	34.91	.12	1.55	.08	4.44	.24	31– 38
Girth of thigh.....	79	53.00	.27	3.56	.19	6.72	.36	47– 60
Girth of knee	79	36.05	.12	1.62	.09	4.49	.24	33– 42
Girth of calf	78	35.05	.14	1.87	.10	5.34	.29	31– 41
Girth of upper arm	79	29.67	.16	2.13	.12	7.18	.39	25– 34
Girth of elbow	75	24.28	.10	1.22	.07	5.03	.28	22– 27
Girth of forearm ..	79	26.49	.10	1.33	.07	5.02	.27	24– 30
Girth of wrist	79	16.47	.05	.68	.04	4.13	.22	15– 19
Breadth of head ..	66	14.90	.05	.63	.04	4.23	.25	13.5– 16
Breadth of neck ..	79	10.94	.04	.59	.03	5.39	.29	9.5– 12
Breadth of shoulders	79	42.75	.17	2.27	.12	5.31	.29	37– 48
Breadth of waist ..	78	25.37	.15	1.97	.11	7.77	.42	22– 32
Breadth of hips ...	79	32.01	.11	1.48	.08	4.62	.25	29– 36
Breadth between nipples	79	19.48	.11	1.49	.08	7.65	.41	15– 23
Shoulder-elbow length	79	36.44	.14	1.90	.10	5.22	.28	32– 40
Elbow-finger length	79	47.30	.15	1.97	.11	4.17	.23	42– 52
Foot length	78	25.80	.09	1.19	.06	4.61	.25	23– 29
Span.............	78	181.93	.52	6.78	.37	3.73	.20	162–197

is not large (79), it is sufficient to permit some conclusions, and there seems little doubt that younger brothers are larger in almost every category. In the two factors in which they fall short of the older brothers, they follow more or less expected differences, for with an increase in stature, head breadth should decrease slightly. This has been shown to be the case among Old Americans, where there is a fairly high correlation between increase in stature and increase in dolichocephaly. The breadth of the waist is probably due to the fact that a general elongation has taken place at the sacrifice of the girth and breadth measurements (Table 65).

TABLE 66

Various Measurements of Younger Brothers — Small Series

	No.	M	p. e.	σ	p. e.	V	p. e.	Range
Weight..........	79	152.45	1.14	15.05	.81	9.87	.53	121–205
Stature	79	177.96	.40	5.22	.28	2.93	.16	167–193
Sitting height	79	91.98	.24	3.16	.17	3.44	.19	83– 98
Navel height......	78	107.24	.33	4.23	.23	3.99	.22	99–118
Pubic height	78	89.16	.30	3.98	.21	4.46	.24	75–100
Sternal height.....	78	145.68	.34	4.44	.24	3.05	.17	134–157
Knee height	78	46.95	.17	2.22	.12	4.73	.26	42– 53
Girth of hips......	79	91.98	.30	3.98	.21	4.33	.23	85–106
Girth of waist.....	79	74.64	.33	4.36	.24	5.84	.32	65– 92
Girth of chest (N)	78	89.86	.33	4.32	.23	4.81	.26	83–100
Girth of chest (F) .	79	95.22	.33	4.38	.24	4.60	.25	87–110
Girth of head	79	57.00	.12	1.52	.08	2.67	.14	53– 61
Girth of neck	79	35.28	.11	1.49	.08	4.22	.23	32– 39
Girth of thigh.....	79	53.78	.26	3.42	.18	6.36	.34	47– 64
Girth of knee	79	36.19	.12	1.64	.09	4.53	.24	33– 42
Girth of calf	78	35.54	.17	2.28	.12	6.42	.35	31– 41
Girth of upper arm.	79	30.36	.17	2.21	.12	7.28	.39	26– 38
Girth of elbow	75	24.91	.10	1.34	.07	5.38	.30	22– 29
Girth of forearm ..	79	26.85	.12	1.53	.08	5.70	.31	23– 30
Girth of wrist	79	16.55	.05	.70	.04	4.23	.23	15– 18
Breadth of head ..	66	14.84	.06	.67	.04	4.52	.27	13.5– 16.5
Breadth of neck ..	79	11.10	.05	.65	.04	5.86	.32	9.5– 13
Breadth of shoulders	79	43.34	.16	2.15	.12	4.96	.27	39– 48
Breadth of waist ..	78	25.33	.12	1.62	.09	6.40	.35	21– 31
Breadth of hips ...	79	32.54	.13	1.69	.09	5.19	.28	29– 39
Breadth between nipples	79	19.71	.11	1.45	.08	7.36	.40	17– 23
Shoulder-elbow length	79	36.49	.12	1.56	.08	4.28	.23	33– 40
Elbow-finger length	79	47.56	.13	1.66	.09	3.49	.19	44– 51
Foot length	78	25.90	.08	1.08	.06	4.17	.23	24– 28
Span.............	78	183.01	.49	6.51	.35	3.56	.19	168–200

Stature

The series in Table 67 shows the means for the different sets of brothers in the large series. There is progressive increase in height from the first-born through to the fifth-born, over a range of nearly two centimeters, from 178.14 to 180.00, with the mean at 178.53, slightly higher even than for men born in the decade 1906–15 (Table 21). The range of all brothers is from 157 to 199, or essentially the same for all sons. The table is not corrected for the annual increase (.08 centimeters), which when introduced gives the results found in Table 68.[1]

TABLE 67

COMPARISON OF STATURE OF BROTHERS BY SENIORITY OF BIRTH — LARGE SERIES

	No.	M	p. e.	σ	p. e.	Range
First	247	178.14	.29	6.63	.20	163–199
Second	247	178.86	.27	6.24	.19	157–196
Third	33	179.10	.68	5.82	.48	169–193
Fourth	5	179.40	...	...	...	172–184
Fifth	1	180.00	...	...	...	...
Mean	533	178.53	...	...	...	157–199

TABLE 68

STATURE OF BROTHERS CORRECTED FOR ANNUAL INCREASE — LARGE SERIES

	M
First	178.14
Second	178.26
Third	178.38
Fourth	178.57
Fifth	178.85

The differences in stature between brothers, although considerable, are not significant. There is successive decrease in the amount of difference between the first and second and second and third brothers. In other words, greater difference exists between the earlier-born than the later-born. The only possible significance might be between the first and third brothers with 1.71, the amount

---

[1] The figures represent the cumulative differences, i. e. the difference between the corrected and uncorrected fifth-brother group, is 1.15 centimeters, or .08 (the annual increase) × 14.4 (the number of years difference). *See* pp. 75–76.

of the difference between the two means expressed in terms of the probable error. Since, however, the difference between the means should be at least three times the probable errors of the differences of the means, its significance is dubious. Only the first, second, and third brothers were used, since the fourth and fifth were inadequately represented.

TABLE 69

DIFFERENCES OF STATURE BETWEEN OLDER AND YOUNGER BROTHERS— LARGE SERIES

	First	Second	Third
Second	.72	...	...
Third	1.31	.59	...
Fourth	1.61	.89	.30

Mean difference .55

TABLE 70

DIFFERENCES IN TERMS OF PROBABLE ERROR OF STATURE FOR OLDER AND YOUNGER BROTHERS — LARGE SERIES

	First	Second	Third
Second	1.82	...	...
Third	1.71	.81	...
Fourth	...	...	...

Mean figure 1.31

TABLE 71

AGE DIFFERENCES OF BROTHERS FOR STATURE — LARGE SERIES

Brothers	1–2	2–3	3–4	4–5	Mean
Years difference	3.80	4.00	2.60	4.00	3.80
Annual increase in stature (.08)..	.30	.32	.21	.32	.30

Obviously, however, the great difficulty in comparing brothers lies in the fact that the annual changes occurring in the population at large must be taken into consideration since there is a mean difference of 3.80 years (Table 71) between each pair of sons. In the present study the various differences between the first and second and third pairs, etcetera, are respectively 3.80, 4.00, 2.60, and 4.00 years, with a mean difference of 3.80.

If we assume, therefore, that the annual increase is the same for the brothers as for the whole population, we may take the mean annual increase, which we have found to be .08, and multiply it by the mean difference in years between the different sets of brothers and hence correct for the difference. In other words, the corrected difference in terms of the probable error would be the difference of the means plus the number of years difference between the different sets of brothers times the annual increase divided by the square root of the sum of the squares of the probable errors of the means. Reduced to equation form we should have the formula:

$$\text{The corrected difference in terms of probable error} = \frac{Ma - Mb + 3.80 \times .08}{\sqrt{\Sigma \, p.e.^2}}.$$

In the present series the differences in years had already been calculated separately; consequently they were multiplied separately by the annual increase. Ordinarily, however, a difference of years of

TABLE 72

DIFFERENCES OF STATURE BETWEEN OLDER AND YOUNGER BROTHERS
CORRECTED FOR ANNUAL INCREASE — LARGE SERIES

	First	Second	Third
Second	.12	...	
Third	.24	.12	...
Fourth	.43	.31	.19

Mean difference .14

3.80 might be allowed, and this multiplied by the annual increase .08 would give .30. This applies only to brothers or sisters, however, and not to brothers and sisters. In the latter case the difference of 3.80 should be halved and multiplied by the annual increase, which would yield .15. We may assume, therefore, that a difference of .15 centimeters must be allowed between any two children born in sequence in any Old American family, the amount being added always to the senior child. The corrected differences and the corrected figures for statistical significance of the different sets of brothers are shown in Tables 72 and 73. The results, although considerably different from the uncorrected material, show nevertheless the same general tendency toward increase with successive juniority.

TABLE 73

DIFFERENCES IN TERMS OF PROBABLE ERROR OF STATURE CORRECTED FOR
ANNUAL INCREASE OF OLDER AND YOUNGER BROTHERS — LARGE SERIES

	First	Second	Third
Second	.31	...	
Third	.32	.16	...
Fourth	...	...	...
Mean figure .23			

Essentially the same results, but even more pronounced, were
obtained for the small series. The uncorrected difference is 1.14 centimeters with 1.92 as the figure for the difference in terms of the
probable error, and the corrected difference (allowing 4.14 years
difference between older and younger instead of 3.80, on account of
the fact that some of the subsequent brothers are third- and fourth-
born) is .81 centimeters, or 1.36 times the probable error. This
compares favorably with the corrected figure, 1.06, for the larger
series between first- and second-born brothers. The correlations for
stature between the oldest and the younger brothers, grouped for
the large series, show a difference between means of .75 centimeters.

TABLE 74

COMPARISON OF STATURE OF OLDER AND YOUNGER BROTHERS BASED ON
PEARSON'S MATERIAL *

	No.	M	p. e.	σ	p. e.	V	p. e.	Range
Older brother	328	174.78	.10	2.60	.07	3.78	.10	160 –201
Younger brother ...	328	174.93	.10	2.75	.07	3.99	.10	152.4–203.2

* Calculated from Tables lviii–lx, Pearson and Lee (1903), pp. 444–446.

Although somewhat lower than for the smaller series, the explanation of the difference is probably the inclusion of a larger percentage
of later-born brothers in the former series, and the consequent error
from the "unearned increment" of annual increase.

In England, Pearson [1] has furnished the only comparative data
of importance. The results of his correlations and their significance
are discussed elsewhere (pp. 89–94). Of interest, however, in a
discussion of comparative stature is the fact that younger brothers

[1] Pearson and Lee (1903), pp. 444–446.

average .15 centimeters higher than older, the averages being 174.78 centimeters for the latter and 174.93 for the former (Table 74). The difference is not significant, since it is only 1.07 times its probable error, but nevertheless shows the same general tendency as that exhibited in the present study. No age is indicated, but it is probable that all were adults, inasmuch as the material is used in comparison with the fathers. If any age difference did exist, it obviously operated in favor of the younger brothers.

Boas [1] has shown in a study of brothers and sisters of Oakland, California, and Toronto, Ontario, that there is a decrease in stature and weight from the oldest to the youngest both in brothers and in sisters. For stature he has arranged his material in tables, with the number of millimeters above or below the mean for each respective age group at one-year intervals from 6.5 to 16.5, with an average progressive decrease between the different sets of sons of .16 centimeters.[2] With a grouping according to oldest and younger brothers he found a difference of .70 centimeters. The tables seem to be perfectly clear when summarized in totals at the foot of the separate columns:

Range of Age Groups	First-born	Second-born	Third-born	Fourth-born	Later-born
6.5–16.5	.45	.40	.19	−.79	−.69

TABLE 75

STATURE DIFFERENCES BETWEEN OLDEST AND YOUNGER BROTHERS (BOAS)

	1	2	3	4
2	−.05	...		
3	−.16	−.11	...	
4	−1.14	−1.09	−.98	...
5	−1.04	−.99	−.88	.10

In commenting upon the causes of the increase noted Boas remarks: "It would seem likely that the greater vigor of the mother at the time of birth of the first child and the greater care bestowed upon the first child during its early childhood may be the cause of the phenomenon. The cares of the increasing household tend to weaken the mother and to decrease the amount of motherly atten-

[1] 1895, pp. 402–404.
[2] Ibid. — calculated from Table 1.

tion devoted to later-born children. It is remarkable that the relation of size existing at the time of birth should be reversed in later life, it having been shown that the weight and length of new-born infants increases from the first-born to the later-born children."

Martin,[1] referring to Boas' material, states that "in one and the same family the first-born are taller than the later-born and the difference is continuous till the fifteenth year; in girls it is continuous till the end of the period of development." Further on he adds the statement, "But also the age of the mother seems to influence the stature and weight of the new-born, in so far as older mothers bring taller and heavier children into the world."

Thus, while admitting that the age of the mother has a certain influence on the size and weight of the child, he fails to apply this to his previous statement for brothers by reason of the fact that the younger were born when the mother was at least one and in most cases from 2 to 5 years older, and would be expected to show the effect of the physical differences in the mother.

TABLE 76

MILLIMETERS ABOVE OR BELOW THE MEAN FOR BOYS OF BOAS' STUDY AND THIS STUDY

Ages	First-born	Second-born	Third-born	Fourth-born	Fifth-born
16.5	−.19	.17	.21	−.20	0
18.2 *	−.09	.03	.15	.34	.62
	(247)	(247)	(33)	(5)	(1)

* Corrected for annual increase. Uncorrected the differences from the mean are as follows:

Age	First-born	Second-born	Third-born	Fourth-born	Fifth-born
18.2	−.39	.33	.57	.87	1.47

Upon examination of Boas' tables, however, the results are not quite so convincing. In the oldest category (16.5 years) there are 116 individuals divided into five groups averaging 23 in each group. The eldest is .19 centimeters below the average, the second .17 above, the third .21 above, the fourth .20 below, and the later-born equal to the average. For the sisters of the same age, however, some sort of negative progression is registered, at least between the oldest and the younger. Both the limited numbers employed and the exceedingly irregular results tend to make the forming of conclusions

[1] 1928, p. 303.

not only questionable but highly problematical. It must be remembered, however, that the annual increase in the general population as a whole, which undoubtedly must be manifest in subadults as well as adults, if taken into consideration would operate in favor of such a hypothesis and considerably strengthen Boas' argument. The comparison between the figures for boys aged 16.5 and the results of the present study (Table 76), in which the average age was 18.2 for all groups of brothers, shows the essential similarity between the two series after the sixteenth year.

It is quite obvious that the results for the boys aged 16.5 run counter to the mean, and considerably weaken the value of Boas' discovery. If we may assume that there is some inherent reason for the similarity of the oldest category and the brothers of the present study, the explanation must lie in some physical or physiological field connected with age. For want of better explanation let us assume that younger brothers tend to arrive at adolescence at a somewhat more advanced age than first-born brothers. Since stature is greatly influenced by adolescence, let us go further and assume that the oldest brothers, who supposedly have matured earlier than the younger, would be taller proportionally to their age, and might therefore be expected to exceed them, even though no chronological priority difference existed. The explanation is only tentative, and requires proof of its validity.

On the basis of our observations and the results of Boas and Fasbender, we may conclude that at birth the younger children are both taller and heavier than the older. In childhood until the period of adolescence the reverse condition exists, and after puberty the younger children, who have matured later than the older, catch up with and again surpass them. The changes in relationships are therefore concomitant with changes in childhood and subsequent maturity.

Weight

In weight the differences are even more marked than in the case of stature. The mean for the oldest brothers in the large series is 148.00 pounds, and for the younger brothers in sequence 150.85, 155.55, 158.50, and 190.00 pounds respectively. The range of all brothers is between 105 and 208 pounds.

From Table 43 we have determined the annual increase in weight at .21 pounds per decade for the students as a whole. Assuming that the brothers represent a fair sample of the students at large, we may, therefore, correct for the annual increase, using the same plan as adopted in the correction of stature. The age differences between the different sets of brothers (3.80, 4.00, 2.60, 4.00 years between first and second, second and third brothers, etcetera), when multiplied by the annual increase and subtracted from the uncorrected means for the series, give the corrected means shown in Table 77.

TABLE 77

WEIGHT OF BROTHERS AND WEIGHT CORRECTED FOR ANNUAL INCREASE —
LARGE SERIES

	No.	M	p. e.	σ	p. e.	Range	M Corrected for Annual Increase
First	251	148.00	.75	17.55	.53	105–200	148.00
Second	251	150.85	.76	17.70	.53	105–208	150.05
Third	33	155.55	2.27	19.40	1.61	125–205	153.91
Fourth	5	158.50	...	...	...	150–170	156.32
Fifth	1	190.00	...	...	...	...	186.98
Mean	541	149.96	...	...	...	105–208	...

TABLE 78

DIFFERENCES OF WEIGHT BETWEEN OLDER AND YOUNGER BROTHERS —
LARGE SERIES

	First	Second	Third
Second	2.85	....	
Third	7.55	4.70	....
Fourth	10.50	7.65	2.95

Mean difference 3.50

The differences are of course cumulative, and consequently the corrected difference between the first and fifth brothers would be 28.98 pounds as opposed to 32.00, the uncorrected figure. The difference (3.02 pounds) represents the total number of years difference (14.40) times the annual increase (.21 pounds).

The differences in weight and the differences in terms of their probable errors are given in Tables 78 and 79. Only the first four sets of brothers were used in calculating the differences, and the first three in the figures for comparative significance.

TABLE 79

DIFFERENCES IN TERMS OF PROBABLE ERROR OF WEIGHT OF OLDER AND
YOUNGER BROTHERS — LARGE SERIES

	First	Second	Third
Second	2.66	....	
Third	3.16	1.96	....
Fourth	....	....	....

Mean figure 2.31

The differences are considerably greater than in the case of
stature as shown by the comparatively high figures for statistical
significance. The mean group figure between first and second and
second and third brothers in stature is 1.31, as opposed to 2.31 in
weight. There is statistically an almost significant difference between the first and second brothers. In the case of the first and third,
with a figure of 3.16, the significance is decidedly more pronounced,
and may be considered as indicating a real difference.

Corrected for annual increase, the differences drop from a mean
of 3.50 pounds to 2.77 pounds between each group of brothers. The
figure for statistical significance drops from 2.31 to 1.76, thus losing
any possible significance which might previously have existed.

TABLE 80

DIFFERENCES OF WEIGHT BETWEEN OLDER AND YOUNGER BROTHERS
CORRECTED FOR ANNUAL INCREASE — LARGE SERIES

	First	Second	Third
Second	2.05	....	
Third	5.91	3.86	....
Fourth	8.32	6.27	2.41

Mean difference 2.77

TABLE 81

DIFFERENCES IN TERMS OF PROBABLE ERROR OF WEIGHT CORRECTED FOR
ANNUAL INCREASE — LARGE SERIES

	First	Second	Third
Second	1.91	....	
Third	2.47	1.61	....
Fourth	....	....	....

Mean figure 1.76

Boas has likewise found that in weight older brothers are heavier than younger. The differences are not as significant as in the case of stature, and are more irregular. As suggested previously, until we have definite data to show that there is retardation in arriving at adolescence on the part of younger brothers, it is difficult to account for the conflict. On the whole it would seem, however, that herein lies the explanation for the discrepancy, which would be even further magnified were the factor of annual increase considered in Boas' material.

Span and Forearm

The only comparable data other than for stature is Pearson's material on span and forearm (Table 82). The results are slightly different, the figures for the present study running considerably higher.

TABLE 82

COMPARISON OF SPAN AND FOREARM OF OLDER AND YOUNGER BROTHERS BASED ON PEARSON'S MATERIAL AND THIS STUDY *

	No.	M	p.e.	σ	p.e.	V	p.e.	Range	Difference from Present Study
Span									
Older brother ..	324	178.36	.08	2.71	.06	4.24	.09	132.1–188	3.57
Younger brother	324	178.38	.11	3.14	.08	4.47	.12	155 –208.28	4.63
Forearm									
Older brother ...	322	47.17	.04	.95	.03	5.12	.14	39.37–55.88	.13
Younger brother	322	47.14	.04	.94	.03	5.06	.14	39.37–55.88	.32

* Calculated from Tables lviii–lxi, Pearson and Lee (1903), pp. 444–446.

COEFFICIENTS OF CORRELATION AND UNIT DIFFERENCES

In correlations again there is considerable variation, as was noticed also between fathers and sons. The highest correlation is in span with a coefficient of .58, and only just below it is stature with .57. We may assume, therefore, that in all probability the cross-correlations between stature and span in the older and younger brothers would be very high (Table 83). Weight is slightly less, with a coefficient of .55. Here again, as in the case of the fathers and sons, the progression from the weight and height correlations down to the breadths and girths is not only marked but steady. In Figures 12 and 13 the correlations for weight and stature of older and for weight and stature of younger brothers are plotted against each other.

The various features grouped according to types of measurements are shown in Table 84, which shows that the weight is greatest, with

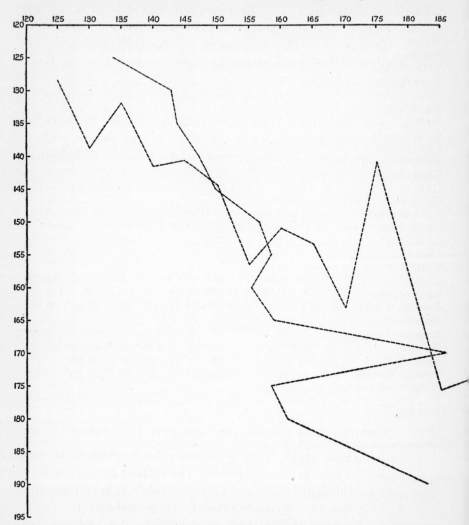

Fig. 12. Correlation between older and younger brothers for weight

a coefficient of .55, and heights and lengths are next with .50, and breadths and girths fall off considerably with coefficients of .35 and .25 respectively, the latter dropping to less than half the figure for weight.

TABLE 83

COEFFICIENTS OF CORRELATION, UNIT DIFFERENCES, AND PERCENTAGES FOR
VARIOUS MEASUREMENTS OF OLDER AND YOUNGER BROTHERS — SMALL SERIES

	No.	r	p. e.	Difference	Percent (Younger Brothers = 100)
Weight..................	79	.55	.05	4.25	97.21
Stature	79	.57	.05	1.14	99.36
Sitting height	79	.46	.06	.38	99.59
Knee height	78	.49	.06	.21	99.72
Pubic height	78	.47	.06	.32	99.64
Navel height............	78	.48	.06	.30	99.42
Sternal height...........	78	.50	.06	.84	99.55
Girth of head	79	.50	.06	.02	98.20
Girth of neck	79	.43	.06	.37	99.07
Girth of chest (N)	78	.29	.07	.24	99.73
Girth of chest (F)	79	.37	.07	.74	99.22
Girth of waist...........	79	.32	.07	1.34	99.96
Girth of hips...........	79	.25	.07	.84	98.95
Girth of thigh...........	79	.37	.07	.78	98.55
Girth of knee	79	.41	.06	.14	99.61
Girth of calf	78	.35	.07	.49	98.62
Girth of upper arm	79	.34	.07	.69	97.73
Girth of elbow	75	.37	.07	.63	97.47
Girth of forearm	79	.29	.07	.36	98.66
Girth of wrist	79	.33	.07	.08	99.52
Breadth of head	66	.29	.08	−.06	100.40
Breadth of neck	79	.21	.07	.16	98.56
Breadth of shoulders	79	.22	.07	.59	98.64
Breadth of waist	79	.27	.07	−.04	100.16
Breadth of hips	79	.25	.07	.53	98.37
Breadth between nipples ..	79	.26	.07	.23	98.80
Shoulder-elbow length	79	.60	.05	.05	99.86
Elbow-finger length	79	.47	.06	.26	99.45
Foot length	78	.39	.06	.10	99.61
Span...................	78	.58	.05	1.08	99.41

TABLE 84

COEFFICIENTS OF CORRELATION FOR VARIOUS GROUPED MEASUREMENTS OF
OLDER AND YOUNGER BROTHERS — SMALL SERIES

	No.	r	p. e.
Weight.........................	79	.55	.05
Heights and lengths	78	.50	.06
Girths	79	.35	.07
Breadths	79	.25	.07
Mean	..	.45	...

In the case of the large series, where again the brothers are grouped into oldest and younger, the correlations are essentially the same as for the small group, but somewhat lower. Weight (.38) is slightly less than stature (.43), but this occurs also among the sisters.

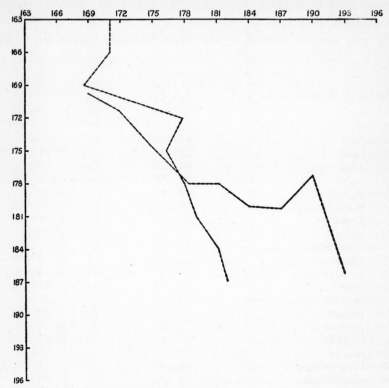

Fig. 13. Correlation between older and younger brothers for stature

TABLE 85

COEFFICIENTS OF CORRELATION FOR WEIGHT AND STATURE OF OLDER AND
YOUNGER BROTHERS — LARGE SERIES

	No.	r	p. e.	Difference *
Weight.............	290	.38	.03	4.40
Stature	291	.43	.03	.75

* Calculated separately to avoid repetition of older brother.

INDICES

The principal indices are on the whole greater in the older brothers. The differences, however, are not very significant, and both series approach quite closely that of the sons of the small series

(Table 86). In relative sitting height the younger brothers are
slightly lower, but in span index somewhat higher.

In arm indices differences are in the same direction as between
fathers and sons. The increase in the upper arm on the part of the
younger sons is actually .05 and in the lower .26, showing clearly
that increase is greater in the lower arm. In indices the relative
upper arm length is 20.61 in the older brothers and 20.51 in the

TABLE 86

VARIOUS MEASUREMENTS IN PROPORTION TO STATURE OF BROTHERS —
SMALL SERIES

	Older Brothers	Younger Brothers
Span	102.89	102.84
Sitting height	51.80	51.69
Navel height	60.48	60.26
Pubic height	50.24	50.10
Sternal height	81.91	81.86
Trunk	31.67	31.76
Upper limb	47.36	47.23
Upper arm	20.61	20.51
Lower arm	26.75	26.73
Knee height	26.43	26.38
Foot length	14.59	14.55
Breadth between nipples	11.02	11.08
Breadth of hips	18.10	18.29
Breadth of shoulders	24.18	24.35
Girth of chest (N)	50.68	50.49
Girth of thigh	29.97	30.22
Girth of waist	41.46	41.94
Girth of hips	51.54	51.69
Upper arm — lower arm	80.85	77.08
Girth of upper-arm — Girth of thigh	55.77	57.41
Girth of knee — girth of calf	102.86	102.78
Knee height — pubic height	23.81	23.72

younger; the relative lower arm length is 26.75 in the older and 26.73
in the younger. The decrease in proportion to stature has been
greater in the relative upper arm length, confirming the previous
conclusions that increase has been greater in the lower arm. The
upper arm-lower arm index, 80.85 in the older brothers and 77.08 in
the younger brothers, further shows this tendency. In leg indices the
same conclusions are reached as in the case of fathers and sons, i. e.
greater increase has occurred in the upper part of the lower limb and

considerably less in the lower. This is in keeping with our other data on extremities, in which with an increase in stature there is greater difference in the proximal segment of the lower extremity. In other body indices likewise the same general results obtain as noticed in the men as a whole.

OBSERVATIONS

Hair Color

The difficulty of using old material is most apparent when dealing with observations and particularly when dealing with pigmentation. It is far easier to determine facial observations, such as nasal form and ear shape, than it is to decide in which category a shade of hair should be classed or the group in which a certain eye color should be placed.

The data is most confusing, and at best can only serve to give a general impression. In Table 87 the numbers and percentages of hair color show very little difference between older and younger

TABLE 87

COEFFICIENT OF MEAN SQUARE CONTINGENCY BETWEEN HAIR COLOR OF OLDER AND YOUNGER BROTHERS

| | Older Brothers | | Younger Brothers | |
	No.	Percent	No.	Percent
Light brown	5	7.35	5	7.35
Medium brown	48	70.59	47	69.12
Dark brown	8	11.77	2	2.94
Black	6	8.82	11	16.18
Red	1	1.47	3	4.41
	68	100.00	68	100.00

C .47

brothers. The younger seem inclined slightly more to the black and red, but the numbers are probably insignificant. On the whole the hair of all brothers is largely medium brown, tending towards dark. The coefficient of mean square contingency .47 is comparatively high, and compares favorably with the results of Pearson,[1] who found a correlation coefficient of .517 ±.020. This is, however, rather below the figure .621 from the material on school boys.[2] Such a high asso-

---

[1] Pearson and Lee (1903), p. 387.
[2] *Ibid.*, p. 388.

ciation shows that pigment is probably even more permanent than measurements, especially stature and weight.

Eye Color

In eye color the association is even more striking than in the case of hair color. The coefficient .61 is considerably higher than that found by Pearson, and would seem to indicate that eye color has much higher fraternal correlation than hair color. The younger brothers tend toward slightly lighter eyes, which is in conflict with the data for hair if we assume that there should exist a high correlation between light hair and light eyes. Of this latter condition, however, we have no proof, and can only surmise that such should be the case. On the whole the results show that the younger brothers have slightly lighter eyes despite their increase in stature. The blue and gray elements predominate in both older and younger brothers, with the browns about equal. The average would appear to be a grayish-blue, with some brown.

TABLE 88

COEFFICIENT OF MEAN SQUARE CONTINGENCY BETWEEN EYE COLOR OF
OLDER AND YOUNGER BROTHERS

| | Older Brothers | | Younger Brothers | |
	No.	Percent	No.	Percent
Blue	23	34.33	32	47.76
Gray	22	32.84	17	25.37
Brown	12	17.91	12	17.91
Dark brown	6	8.96	1	1.49
Green-brown	3	4.47	2	2.99
Black	1	1.49	3	4.48
	67	100.00	67	100.00

C .61

CONCLUSIONS

PARENTAL RESEMBLANCE AND ALTERATION IN TYPE

From our data we have concluded that the present generation of males is considerably taller and heavier than the past generation, and in general bodily measurements exceeds it in almost every character. Increase has been steady for the past four generations, irrespective of relationship, both in stature and in weight, at the mean rate for stature of about .08 centimeters per annum, with a statistically significant difference occurring every 8½ years, and for weight of .21 pounds per annum with a statistically significant increase every 11½ years. Proportionally the younger men are slenderer, especially in the hips. In the shoulders they are somewhat broader. Head breadth has decreased, and is probably compensated for by head length, as would be expected since increase in stature is fairly highly correlated with increase in long-headedness. Trunk length has not increased as much as leg length, and in the latter there has been more increase in the upper than in the lower segment. In relative sitting height the fathers have a higher index than the sons, and in this respect the sons have accentuated the male tendency to be longer in the legs in proportion to height. In other features also, such as decrease in proportional hip measurements and increase in thoracic region, this has taken place. In parental resemblance, the degree of relationship between fathers and sons is about ¼ to 1, with a correlation of .25, for all body measurements, but in stature, span, and forearm the coefficient is .34. The correlation with grandfathers and great-grandfathers was not calculated because of the doubtfulness of the material. Were the correlations to be made, however, it is likely that essentially the same results would prevail as those obtained by Lutz,[1] who concluded that inheritance of likeness grows less with each successive generation.

TABLE 89

COEFFICIENTS OF CORRELATION FOR VARIOUS MEASUREMENTS OF FATHERS AND SONS GROUPED — SMALL SERIES

	r	p. e.
Weight	.29	.03
Heights and lengths *	.34	.03
Girths	.24	.03
Breadths	.17	.03
Total	.25	.03

* Including stature, various heights, length of upper and lower arms, foot, and span.

The figures for the large series are somewhat better. For weight the coefficient is .32 and for stature .43, with a mean of .375.

[1] F. E. Lutz, *Note on the Influence of Change in Sex on the Intensity of Heredity,* Biometrika, II (1903), 236.

TABLE 90

COEFFICIENTS OF CORRELATION FOR WEIGHT AND STATURE OF FATHERS
AND SONS — LARGE SERIES

	No.	r	p. e.
Weight...................	1459	.32	.016
Stature	1453	.43	.01
Mean	..	.375	..

Pearson determined the mean coefficient of heredity at .463, using the three measurements stature, span, and forearm. In the present study for these three measurements the mean is .350. There are two possible explanations for the difference: first, the difference in age between fathers and sons in the former series; second, the fact that considerable morphological changes have taken place as a whole during the past generation here in America. When other body measurements are considered, however, the mean figure drops to .25, or practically one-half of Pearson's figure. Our conclusion is, therefore, that in mean inheritance of all measurable characters the sons are similar to their fathers in the relation of $\frac{1}{4}$ to 1. It is impossible to say how long the present tendency will continue. If we may presume, on the basis of the present decline in annual stature increment, that other factors are also decreasing, it is more than likely that the coefficient of parental likeness will increase during the next generation.

It is also likely that there are certain modifiers which have been introduced to affect the inheritance of various factors. Davenport,[1] in a study of heredity of stature from the purely hereditary point of view, concludes that no simple mendelian laws of inheritance as a whole can apply for stature — or, one would be inclined to add, for other measurements.

The causes operative in the alteration of type and the passing on of certain characteristics from one generation to another are much more complex than they have hitherto been considered, and merit most careful consideration.

[1] C. B. Davenport, *Inheritance of Stature*, Genetics, II, 313-389.

FRATERNAL RESEMBLANCE

Pearson, in his important work *On the Laws of Inheritance in Man*,[1] has produced the only data which can be compared with the present series. He found that resemblance in siblings was greater for stature and span than for forearm or eye color, and that the resemblance of brothers and sisters seemed on the average slightly less than between siblings of the same sex. He concludes that although considerable variety is shown the average degree of hereditary resemblance in human siblings is .5, and summarizes his results as follows:

(1) The degree of resemblance of brethren is much the same for all characters.

(2) The two sexes appear to be equally influenced by heredity.

(3) The intensity of fraternal correlation in man is close to .5, possibly slightly greater. But for practical purposes we may conveniently work with .5 as a round number.

A comparison of the coefficients obtained by Pearson and those of the present study are shown in Table 91. It is quite apparent that the results are in substantial agreement. The slightly higher correlation in the present series is probably due to the smaller sample employed, since in the case of the large series the coefficient drops to .43 for stature. The means for the two series, .517 and .54, are so close that for all practical purposes they may be counted the same.

TABLE 91

COMPARISON OF CORRELATION COEFFICIENTS FOR DIRECT FRATERNAL HEREDITY

	Pearson	Present Study Small Series	Large Series
Stature	.511 ± .028	.57 ± .05	.43 ± .03
Span..........	.549 ± .026	.58 ± .05	..
Forearm	.491 ± .029	.47 ± .06	..
Mean	.517	.54	..

The difficulty in assuming .5 as a standard is apparent, however, when other measurements are employed. As noted above, there is successive falling off in resemblance from lengths to girths and breadths, so that when these have been taken into consideration the mean coefficient drops very considerably to an average of .43.

[1] Pearson and Lee (1903), pp. 444–446.

It appears, therefore, that we cannot take the more stable measurements of stature and span as indicative of the degree of similarity, but must take into consideration all bodily measurements. A further modifying factor must be considered. In the case of stature, the annual increase had considerable effect on the means of the different sets of brothers. Assuming, therefore, that the influence would extend to other measurements as well, we may conclude that the correction, since it tends to equalize the differences in stature, would tend also to equalize the differences of the other measurements. Since equalizing would probably increase the coefficient of correlation, we may assume that the mean correlation would be raised from .43 to, say, .45.

In conclusion, therefore, we may summarize the results as follows. There seems to be somewhat closer resemblance between brothers than between fathers and sons. Older brothers are both shorter and lighter than younger brothers, who in progressive sequence are found to be both taller and heavier, and have the majority of other bodily measurements in their favor. Further, resemblance is greatest in span, stature, and weight, and becomes progressively less significant for the various heights and lengths, but in general the relationship for these characters may be considered as .5 or slightly above. For girths and breadths the correlation drops very considerably and brings the mean figure to .43. If corrected for the factor of annual increase, the coefficient would probably be in the neighborhood of .45. In observations, results show that hair color and eye color are more highly correlated than measurements.

PARENTAL INHERITANCE AND FRATERNAL RESEMBLANCE

Having determined fraternal inheritance to be approximately .45 and the association of observations to be over .50, it is possible to compare fraternal and parental inheritance.

In comparing parental inheritance with fraternal resemblance in different species, Pearson found that although in man the relationships were fairly similar, in certain animals the fraternal correlations were far below the parental. He accounts for the difference on the basis of prepotencies, which he has divided into sex, unit, and intermittent. His conclusions are that hair color and eye color are sexually prepotent factors, as opposed to the measurements of stature, span, and forearm. He would distinguish, therefore, between observable and mensurable characters. Unit prepotency exists in his definition when one or the other mate is prepotent, owing to the possession of some physical character other than sexual. In intermittent prepotency one mate may be temporarily prepotent in one mating, but a reversal may occur in subsequent matings. Pearson concludes that apart from sex prepotency neither unit nor intermittent prepotency influences correlations of parental inheritance. If, therefore, the parental resemblance is greater than the fraternal, the explanation is to be found in the differing amounts of unit and intermittent prepotency, which, theoretically, by the laws of chance should not affect correlations between parents and offspring.

Since, however, in both Pearson's work and the present study fraternal correlation exceeds parental, it may be adduced that man is not influenced by the same factors which govern the rest of the animal kingdom.

Chapter III

FEMALE STUDENTS

A LL measurements of female students are from Wellesley, Vassar, Smith, and Mt. Holyoke Colleges. The material was gathered from records of the gymnasia and the departments of physical education of the different institutions, and treated similarly to the data on men students.

MOTHERS AND DAUGHTERS

AGE

The average age of the 501 mothers from all colleges in the present study is 18.76 years, with the mean ages for the different colleges ranging from 18 to 19.5 years. For daughters, numbering 570, the average is 17.88 and the range from 17.5 to 18 years. For convenience the means may be reduced to round numbers, the mothers to 19 and the daughters to 18. The actual difference of .88 years is thus raised to one year (Table 92).

TABLE 92

AGES OF WOMEN FROM VARIOUS COLLEGES

College	Mothers			Daughters		
	No.	M	σ	No.	M	σ
Wellesley	205	19.54	1.35	241	17.91	.91
Vassar	208	18.01	1.14	227	17.52	.84
Smith	53	18.30	1.17	62	17.86	.92
Mt. Holyoke...........	35	19.40	1.63	40	18.07	.90
Total	501	18.76	1.25	570	17.88	.88

The women are on the average practically a year younger than the men (large series), the actual difference between the fathers (19.65) and mothers being .89 centimeters, and the difference between the sons (18.51) and daughters .63 centimeters, both in favor of the men. Since, however, the correlation between age and different measurements, more particularly stature, is negative in the case of women and insignificant in the case of men, the consideration of age differences may for all practical purposes be dismissed. This anomalous condition is explained elsewhere, and need concern us here only in determining the reliability of uncorrected comparisons.

The standard deviations for the mothers, with a mean of 1.25 and a range of 1.14–1.63, show a greater dispersion than those for daughters, with a mean of .88 and a range of .84–.92. This is to be expected, in view of the fact that the older generation was measured over the whole of the college period, whereas the daughters were measured upon matriculation. Both figures are lower than those of the men (large series), who show a standard deviation of 2.26 for the fathers and 1.27 for the sons.

Correlation of Age with Various Measurements

The measurements used in computing correlations between age and different measurements were limited to Wellesley College. The numbers proved sufficient to give an accurate idea of the entire series, and since in almost all cases the results were negative or insignificant it seemed unnecessary to obtain comparative data from the other colleges.

The various measurements correlated with age for both mothers and daughters show in almost every instance a negative result. We have already noticed this condition in the case of the men (smaller series), where there is an average correlation for all measurements with age of .01 for the fathers and −.01 for the sons. The results obtained for the women's series, −.04 for both mothers and daughters, are slightly but not significantly more negative. The difference may possibly be accounted for by the fact that in the correlations for weight and for heights and lengths with age, both men and women show approximately the same relationships, indicating that the drop in the mean for the women is probably due to the inclusion of the correlations for girths and breadths, as will be apparent on comparing Tables 94 and 9.

The only positive correlations for the mothers are in sitting height, knee height, girth of head, girth of waist, girth of calf, breadth of head, lower arm length, and span. Of the remainder, three are intermediate (0), while the rest run as high as −.21. This last measurement, breadth of neck, is in fact the only correlation showing any significant variation from the mean. It is difficult to account for this single variation unless one assumes that there is some connection between age and the use of high whalebone collars, which probably the majority of the women wore while in college (1880–1900).

TABLE 93

CoEFFICIENTS OF CORRELATION FOR AGE AND VARIOUS MEASUREMENTS FOR MOTHERS AND DAUGHTERS — WELLESLEY COLLEGE

	Mothers			Daughters		
	No.	r	p. e.	No.	r	p. e.
Weight.................	205	−.07	.05	241	−.03	.04
Stature	205	−.06	.05	241	−.11	.04
Sitting height	165	.06	.05	50	−.13	.09
Knee height	165	.007	.05			
Pubic height	165	−.02	.05			
Navel height............	165	−.04	.05			
Sternal height...........	199	−.06	.05			
Girth of head	165	.03	.05			
Girth of neck	165	0	00			
Girth of chest (N)	205	−.004	.05			
Girth of chest (F)	205	0	00	152	.02	.06
Girth of waist...........	205	.02	.05	131	.005	.06
Girth of hips............	165	−.08	.05			
Girth of thigh...........	165	−.02	.05			
Girth of knee	165	−.11	.05			
Girth of calf	165	.007	.05			
Girth of upper arm	165	−.08	.05			
Girth of elbow	165	−.07	.05			
Girth of wrist	165	−.05	.05			
Breadth of head	165	−.07	.05			
Breadth of neck	165	−.21	.05			
Breadth of shoulders......	165	−.06	.05			
Breadth of waist	165	−.09	.05			
Breadth of hips	165	−.10	.05			
Breadth between nipples ..	165	0	00			
Shoulder-elbow length	165	−.04	.05			
Elbow-finger length	163	.03	.05			
Length of foot	165	−.10	.05			
Span....................	165	.01	.05			

When grouped according to types of measurements the results, although still not significant, show possible trends. With the exception of weight there is progressively less correlation from heights and lengths (−.026) to girths (−.036) and breadths (−.076). This decrease in amount of relationship is to be accounted for by the fact that there is more variability in girth and breadth measurements with age than in weight or heights and lengths. The same condition obtains for the correlations between fathers and sons. In the latter instance the variability can be accounted for by the considerable increases in girth and breadth measurements.

TABLE 94

COEFFICIENTS OF CORRELATION FOR AGE AND VARIOUS GROUPED MEASUREMENTS FOR MOTHERS AND DAUGHTERS — WELLESLEY COLLEGE

	Mothers		Daughters	
	r	p. e.	r	p. e.
Weight.................	−.07	.05	−.03	.04
Heights and lengths * ...	−.026	.05	−.11	.05
Girths	−.036	.05	.012	.06
Breadths	−.076	.05		
Total mean	−.04	...	−.04	

* Including stature, various heights, length of upper and lower arms, foot, and span.

For the daughters the results are somewhat contradictory, although statistically not significant, the lengths and heights showing a relatively high negative correlation and girths a slight positive result. Upon examination of the larger table (93), however, it will be observed that the two measurements, girth of chest (full) and girth of waist, which give positive coefficients, .012, are also .01 in the case of the mothers. The greater negative correlations are therefore in the other girth measurements.

More specific comparisons are given in Tables 95 and 96, where the frequencies, means, and probable errors of the means are listed, in the case of the mothers for the ages 18, 19, and 20, and of the daughters for the ages 17, 18, and 19 — the only age groups with frequencies large enough for use. In the daughters the measurement for sitting height was rejected on account of the small size of the groups.

The two most significant series in Table 95, the one positive, the other negative, show respective increases and decreases in the age group comparisons. Sitting height in the mothers increases from 84.40 at 18 to 84.46 at 19 and 85.11 at 20. On the other hand, in the case of breadth of neck there is a consistent decrease from 9.73 at 18 to 9.68 at 19 and 9.43 at 20. In the case of the daughters (Table 96), the only feature of interest is the consistent increase of weight, from 123.01 at 17 to 123.56 at 18 and 124.74 at 19.

TABLE 95

COMPARISON OF VARIOUS MEASUREMENTS AT DIFFERENT AGES—
WELLESLEY COLLEGE MOTHERS

	Age 18			Age 19			Age 20		
	No.	M	p. e.	No.	M	p. e.	No.	M	p. e.
Weight..............	62	123.79	1.47	64	120.	1.08	41	120.16	1.38
Stature	62	162.17	.38	64	160.67	.41	41	160.73	.57
Sitting height	51	84.40	.24	52	84.46	.27	36	85.11	.31
Knee height	51	40.82	.16	52	40.82	.17	36	40.78	.21
Pubic height	51	78.54	.30	52	78.07	.36	36	77.97	.47
Navel height.........	51	97.40	.38	52	96.36	.39	36	96.93	.52
Sternal height.......	60	132.76	.37	64	131.77	.36	42	131.16	.52
Girth of head	51	55.07	.14	52	55.22	.13	36	54.69	.17
Girth of neck	51	30.25	.07	52	30.46	.12	36	30.22	.14
Girth of chest (N) ...	62	73.58	.53	64	73.13	.50	41	73.36	.57
Girth of chest (F)	62	80.54	.38	64	80.28	.35	41	80.45	.44
Girth of waist........	62	62.05	.36	64	61.79	.36	41	62.27	.41
Girth of hips.........	51	91.44	.64	52	91.94	.67	36	91.57	.67
Girth of thigh........	51	54.68	.46	52	53.93	.39	36	54.67	.40
Girth of knee	51	35.29	.26	52	34.64	.25	36	34.71	.23
Girth of calf	51	33.65	.23	52	33.45	.20	36	33.39	.21
Girth of upper arm ...	51	26.25	.24	52	25.92	.23	36	25.68	.21
Girth of elbows	51	22.31	.12	52	22.22	.13	36	22.22	.13
Girth of forearm	51	21.78	.16	52	21.62	.16	36	21.68	.14
Girth of wrist	51	14.65	.06	52	14.63	.06	36	14.47	.07
Breadth of head	51	14.73	.04	52	14.74	.05	36	14.60	.07
Breadth of neck	51	9.73	.05	52	9.68	.04	36	9.43	.07
Breadth of shoulders .	51	36.68	.16	52	37.24	.22	36	36.55	.20
Breadth of waist	51	21.68	.15	52	21.71	.14	36	21.37	.17
Breadth of hips	50	32.78	.26	53	33.19	.28	36	32.83	.28
Breadth between nipples	51	20.46	.17	52	20.00	.16	36	20.25	.23
Shoulder-elbow length.	51	33.84	.12	52	33.71	.13	36	33.58	.18
Elbow-finger length ..	51	42.12	.16	52	42.08	.16	36	41.90	.24
Foot length	51	23.47	.10	52	23.55	.10	36	22.96	.13
Span................	51	163.08	.55	52	163.13	.57	36	161.75	.76

TABLE 96

COMPARISON OF VARIOUS MEASUREMENTS AT DIFFERENT AGES—
WELLESLEY COLLEGE DAUGHTERS

	Age 17			Age 18			Age 19		
	No.	M	p. e.	No.	M	p. e.	No.	M	p. e.
Weight..............	71	123.01	.87	101	123.56	.98	52	124.74	1.47
Stature	69	164.80	.40	102	163.63	.34	52	163.96	.43
Girth of chest (F)	39	84.85	.46	63	84.66	.35	41	85.38	.41
Girth of waist........	34	64.74	.51	50	65.2	.44	38	64.80	.46

The results thus far, in comparing the correlations between age and various measurements, have shown that women students behave in much the same way as do the men students. A comparison of the age curve lines for mothers and daughters and fathers and sons in Figure 2 will show that as regards stature the similarity is very marked. The mothers and daughters assume almost identical curves, with the greatest height in the seventeenth year, and the fathers and sons likewise, with the greatest height in the eighteenth year. This difference of one year, as we have noted, is due to the fact that the women enter college when approximately one year younger than the men.

The lack of harmony between the lines joining the means of the age groups for the men and women and the remaining lines, both smoothed and unsmoothed, shows the difference, as noted on page 15, between the student and the non-selected classes. It is probable that, if groups of large enough size could be found for the ages above 20 in the case of the mothers and above 19 in the case of the daughters, there would be a fairly regular increase up to about the age of 25, — the normal age for the commencement of decline in stature for women, — when the tendency would be to follow the normal curve in conformity with the random sample.

In conclusion, therefore, we may assume that for student groups there is a mean negative correlation between all measurements and age, irrespective of generations. The only possible exception to be noted is the case of the breadth of the neck in the mothers, which may or may not be significant. Grouped according to types, the more nearly positive correlations are for height and length measurements, while the girth measurements are slightly more negative, and the breadth measurements in some cases show marked negative correlation. The results are essentially the same as those for the men's series, and further strengthen the suggestion that students as a whole represent a very highly specialized group and cannot be compared favorably with random samples from the general population.

Comparisons between Various Colleges

Mothers

In making a comparison of the mothers from Wellesley and Vassar Colleges (see Tables 97–100) it is interesting to note that the Wellesley mothers exceed the Vassar mothers in twenty out of thirty measurements. It would appear that the Wellesley women were on the whole slightly heavier, whereas the Vassar women were taller, bigger in the chest and hips, and inclined to be longer in the limbs. In brief, the Wellesley women were stouter and shorter, but less developed in the chest and hips.

In the case of the Smith College mothers, both stature and weight are in excess of the Vassar women, and their stature exceeds that of all of the other college mothers. The Mt. Holyoke mothers in both measurements are significantly smaller, although the sample can hardly be considered adequate.

TABLE 97

CONSTANTS FOR VARIOUS MEASUREMENTS — WELLESLEY COLLEGE MOTHERS

	No.	M	p. e.	σ	p. e.	V	p. e.	Range
Weight	205	121.25	.71	15.25	.50	12.55	.41	86 −185
Stature	205	161.28	.23	4.97	.16	3.08	.10	148 −173.5
Sitting height	165	84.58	.15	2.78	.10	3.28	.12	77.5− 90
Knee height	165	40.79	.10	1.94	.07	4.76	.18	35.5− 46
Pubic height	165	78.1	.20	3.76	.14	4.82	.18	69. − 88
Navel height	165	96.67	.23	4.27	.16	4.42	.16	86. −106.5
Sternal height	199	131.94	.21	4.41	.15	3.34	.11	120.5−145.5
Girth of head	165	55.09	.07	1.41	.05	2.56	.09	51.5− 60
Girth of neck	165	30.51	.08	1.43	.05	4.69	.17	27 − 36.5
Girth of chest (N)	205	73.91	.27	5.77	.19	7.81	.26	60.5− 93
Girth of chest (F)	205	80.68	.20	4.34	.14	5.38	.18	72. − 95
Girth of waist	205	62.15	.19	3.96	.13	6.37	.21	53.5− 76
Girth of hips	165	91.21	.34	6.46	.24	7.08	.26	74. −110
Girth of thigh	165	54.33	.10	1.80	.07	3.31	.12	44. − 68
Girth of knee	165	34.83	.13	2.45	.09	7.04	.26	29. − 46.5
Girth of calf	165	33.59	.12	2.14	.09	6.01	.22	28.5− 44
Girth of upper arm	165	25.95	.12	2.29	.08	8.82	.33	21. − 34
Girth of elbow	165	22.23	.08	1.27	.05	5.71	.21	19.5− 26.5
Girth of forearm	165	21.73	.06	1.07	.04	4.92	.18	18. − 26
Girth of wrist	165	14.6	.03	.65	.02	4.45	.16	13. − 16.5
Breadth of head	165	14.73	.03	.54	.02	3.67	.14	13. − 16
Breadth of neck	165	9.61	.03	.57	.02	5.93	.22	8. − 11
Breadth of shoulders	165	36.81	.10	1.95	.07	5.30	.20	32.5− 43.5
Breadth of waist	165	21.68	.09	1.73	.06	7.98	.30	17.5− 25.5
Breadth of hips	165	32.73	.14	2.73	.10	8.34	.31	26. − 40
Breadth between nipples	165	20.24	.09	1.87	.07	9.23	.34	16. − 27
Shoulder-elbow length	165	33.65	.05	1.03	.04	3.06	.11	30. − 39
Elbow-finger length	163	42.08	.10	1.93	.07	4.59	.17	37.5− 50
Foot length	165	23.36	.06	1.12	.04	4.80	.18	19.5− 26
Span	165	162.60	.36	6.70	.25	4.10	.15	147. −183.5

TABLE 98

CONSTANTS FOR VARIOUS MEASUREMENTS — VASSAR COLLEGE MOTHERS

	No.	M	p. e.	σ	p. e.	V	p. e.	Range
Weight..........	208	120.55	.72	15.30	.50	12.69	.42	85 −180
Stature	208	161.84	.27	5.70	.19	3.52	.12	134 −176
Sitting height	201	85.31	.13	2.69	.09	3.15	.11	79 − 94
Knee height	198	43.18	.12	2.56	.09	5.93	.20	35 − 49
Pubic height	192	76.83	.19	3.93	.13	5.12	.17	67 − 88
Navel height......	153	96.46	.23	4.24	.17	4.40	.17	84 −109
Sternal height.....	198	132.11	.24	5.01	.17	3.79	.13	120 −146
Girth of head	199	54.42	.06	1.35	.05	2.48	.08	50.5− 57.5
Girth of neck	208	30.39	.07	1.53	.05	5.03	.17	26.5− 35
Girth of chest (N)	208	77.38	.20	4.18	.14	5.40	.18	67 − 94
Girth of chest (F) .	208	82.10	.20	4.19	.14	5.10	.17	73 − 95
Girth of waist.....	208	61.07	.20	4.23	.14	6.93	.23	52 − 80
Girth of hips......	208	93.22	.30	6.40	.21	6.87	.23	72 −114
Girth of thigh.....	207	53.90	.19	4.07	.13	7.55	.25	41 − 64
Girth of knee	207	34.00	.13	2.66	.09	7.82	.26	26 − 43
Girth of calf	207	32.98	.11	2.32	.08	7.04	.23	22 − 40
Girth of upper arm	207	25.92	.10	2.23	.07	8.60	.28	21.5− 33
Girth of elbow	207	21.03	.07	1.52	.05	7.23	.24	17.5− 25.5
Girth of forearm ..	207	22.54	.07	1.39	.05	6.17	.20	19 − 26.5
Girth of wrist	206	14.17	.04	.79	.03	5.58	.18	12 − 16.5
Breadth of head ..	199	14.71	.03	.53	.02	3.60	.12	14 − 16.5
Breadth of neck ..	203	9.32	.03	.63	.02	6.76	.22	7.5− 11
Breadth of shoulders	207	36.70	.08	1.72	.06	4.69	.05	32 − 40.5
Breadth of waist ..	206	21.17	.08	1.66	.05	7.84	.26	14.5− 26
Breadth of hips ...	205	33.24	.10	2.22	.07	6.68	.22	23 − 42
Breadth between nipples	32	17.91	.23	1.90	.16	10.61	.89	10.5− 20.5
Shoulder-elbow length	200	33.31	.08	1.59	.05	4.77	.16	29 − 37.5
Elbow-finger length	198	42.15	.09	1.86	.06	4.41	.15	31.5− 45.5
Length of foot	199	23.28	.05	1.05	.04	4.51	.15	20.5− 26.5
Span.............	182	162.15	.31	6.22	.22	3.84	.13	146 −175

Grouped by different measurements, the standard deviations and coefficients of variation show considerable differences. In all measurements except breadths the Wellesley mothers show considerably less deviation and variation than the Vassar mothers. In comparisons of total mean deviations and variations the relationship is again the same, with a greater difference in the case of the Vassar mothers.

TABLE 99

COMPARISON OF TRAITS BETWEEN WELLESLEY AND VASSAR MOTHERS

(Cross indicating greater measurement)

	Wellesley	Vassar
Weight.....................	×	—
Stature	—	×
Sitting height	—	×
Knee height	—	×
Pubic height	×	—
Navel height..............	×	—
Sternal height..............	—	×
Girth of head	×	—
Girth of neck	×	—
Girth of chest (N)	—	×
Girth of chest (F)	—	×
Girth of waist.............	×	—
Girth of hips..............	—	×
Girth of thigh.............	×	—
Girth of knee	×	—
Girth of calf	×	—
Girth of upper arm	×	—
Girth of elbow	×	—
Girth of forearm	—	×
Girth of wrist	×	—
Breadth of head	×	—
Breadth of neck	×	—
Breadth of shoulders	×	—
Breadth of waist	×	—
Breadth of hips	—	×
Breadth between nipples	×	—
Shoulder-elbow length	×	—
Elbow-fingertip length	—	×
Length of foot	×	—
Span.....................	×	—
Totals	20	10

TABLE 100

COMPARISON OF VARIOUS MEASUREMENTS GROUPED — WELLESLEY AND
VASSAR MOTHERS

	Wellesley		Vassar	
	σ	V	σ	V
Weight.............	15.25	12.55	15.30	12.69
Heights and lengths ..	3.29	3.72	3.48	4.34
Girths	2.69	5.70	2.83	6.29
Breadths	1.56	6.74	1.44	6.69
Mean	3.08	5.28	3.19	5.93

TABLE 101

WEIGHT AND STATURE — SMITH COLLEGE MOTHERS

	No.	M	p. e.	σ	p. e.	V	p. e.
Weight......	51	120.59	1.52	16.20	1.09	13.43	.90
Stature	53	162.33	.45	4.83	.32	2.98	.20

TABLE 102

WEIGHT AND STATURE — MT. HOLYOKE COLLEGE MOTHERS

	No.	M	p. e.	σ	p. e.	V	p. e.
Weight......	35	117.43	1.64	14.40	1.17	12.26	.99
Stature	35	160.96	.56	4.89	.40	3.04	.25

Daughters

The daughters show considerably more uniformity in stature and slightly less in weight than the mothers. In all the groups, however, the relationship is the same, for with increase in stature there is corresponding increase in weight.

In the case of other measurements the only ones that can be compared are sitting height, girth of chest normal and expanded, and girth of waist. These measurements are restricted, as in the case of the mothers, to Wellesley and Vassar Colleges. In all measurements except girth of chest (full) the Vassar daughters exceed the Wellesley. There does not appear to be the same relationship existing between the daughters as was apparent in the case of the mothers. In relative sitting height the difference is insignificant, the proportion running slightly higher in the Vassar measurements.

TABLE 103

VARIOUS MEASUREMENTS — WELLESLEY COLLEGE DAUGHTERS

	No.	M	p. e.	σ	p. e.	V	p. e.	Range
Weight..........	241	123.5	.60	13.86	.44	11.22	.35	90.5–174.5
Stature	241	164.06	.22	5.22	.17	3.18	.10	150 –178
Sitting height	50	86.25	.26	2.78	.18	3.22	.22	81 – 93
Girth of chest (N)	24	77.35	.43	3.08	.30	3.98	.39	71 – 89
Girth of chest (F) .	152	84.96	.22	4.03	.16	4.74	.18	74 – 93
Girth of waist.....	131	64.94	.26	4.35	.18	6.70	.28	56.5– 77
Relative sitting height		52.57						

TABLE 104

VARIOUS MEASUREMENTS — VASSAR COLLEGE DAUGHTERS

	No.	M	p. e.	σ	p. e.	V	p. e.	Range
Weight..............	229	125.25	.74	16.45	.53	13.13	.42	86–190
Stature	228	165.10	.26	5.75	.18	2.48	.11	151–180
Sitting height	148	86.94	.15	2.81	.11	3.23	.13	80– 96
Girth of neck	160	30.12	.10	1.87	.07	6.21	.24	24– 35
Girth of chest (N)	229	78.08	.22	4.98	.16	6.55	.21	65– 92
Girth of chest (F)	229	84.88	.21	4.72	.15	5.56	.17	74–100
Girth of waist........	221	65.29	.23	5.16	.17	7.90	.25	51– 86
Girth of hips..........	223	93.42	.29	6.50	.21	6.96	.22	77–114
Girth of forearm	137	22.92	.11	1.88	.08	8.20	.34	16– 29
Girth of upper arm	137	26.18	.16	2.68	.11	10.24	.42	19– 37
Breadth of shoulders ..	162	36.89	.10	1.88	.07	5.10	.19	31– 43
Breadth of waist	155	21.67	.10	1.77	.07	8.17	.31	17– 28
Breadth of hips	29	30.28	.24	1.94	.17	6.41	.57	27– 35
Relative sitting height		52.65						

In Table 105 the different measurements on daughters of Wellesley and Vassar Colleges are compared. In every measurement except girth of chest (full), the Vassar daughters exceed the Wellesley. In general the reverse was true of the mothers, with the exception of stature.

TABLE 105

COMPARISON OF TRAITS BETWEEN WELLESLEY AND VASSAR DAUGHTERS

(Cross indicates greater measurement)

	Wellesley	Vassar
Weight....................	—	×
Stature	—	×
Sitting height	—	×
Girth of chest (N)	—	×
Girth of chest (F)	×	—
Girth of waist.............	—	×
Totals	1	5

TABLE 106

VARIOUS MEASUREMENTS — SMITH COLLEGE DAUGHTERS

	No.	M	p. e.	σ	p. e.	V	p. e.	Range
Weight..........	62	127.84	1.26	14.70	.90	11.50	.70	95.5–166
Stature	62	164.99	.51	5.94	.36	3.60	.22	15.2–179

TABLE 107

VARIOUS MEASUREMENTS — MT. HOLYOKE COLLEGE DAUGHTERS

	No.	M	p. e.	σ	p. e.	V	p. e.	Range
Weight.........	40	122.79	1.86	17.40	1.31	13.28	1.00	84.5–163.5
Stature	40	163.43	.50	4.71	.35	2.88	.22	153–177.5

TABLE 108

WEIGHT AND STATURE OF ALL WOMEN'S COLLEGES COMPARED — MOTHERS

	Wellesley			Vassar			Smith			Mt. Holyoke		
	No.	M	p. e.	No.	M	p. e.	No.	M	p. e.	No.	M	p. e.
Weight...	205	121.25	.71	208	120.55	.72	51	120.59	1.52	35	117.43	1.64
Stature ..	205	161.28	.23	208	161.84	.27	53	162.33	.45	35	160.96	.56

TABLE 109

WEIGHT AND STATURE OF ALL WOMEN'S COLLEGES COMPARED — DAUGHTERS

	Wellesley			Vassar			Smith			Mt. Holyoke		
	No.	M	p. e.	No.	M	p. e.	No.	M	p. e.	No.	M	p. e.
Weight...	241	123.5	.60	229	125.25	.74	62	127.84	1.26	40	122.79	1.86
Stature ..	241	164.06	.22	228	165.10	.26	62	164.99	.51	40	163.43	.50

TABLE 110

DIFFERENCES IN WEIGHT AND STATURE BETWEEN MOTHERS AND DAUGHTERS —
VARIOUS WOMEN'S COLLEGES

	Wellesley	Vassar	Smith	Mt. Holyoke
Weight..............	2.25	4.70	7.25	5.36
Stature	2.78	3.26	2.66	1.47

COMPARISON OF STATISTICAL CONSTANTS OF THIRTY MEASUREMENTS FOR ALL COLLEGES

In the following tables the means of the mothers and daughters of all colleges are compared. With the exception of stature, weight, and sitting height few comparative data are used, since a comparison of other measurements without taking these into consideration would be of little value. It has been impossible to secure data on American women students of different periods in which the above-named factors are constant, and hence, until some suitable correction for all measurements both for age and for period of measurement can be devised, it will not be practicable to make direct comparisons.

Table 111 shows the measurements of all mothers, Table 112 the measurements of all daughters, and Table 113 the two compared.

In the discussion of weight and stature the order is reversed, as in the case of the men's series, the more important and constant measurement of stature being considered first.

TABLE 111

VARIOUS MEASUREMENTS — MOTHERS OF ALL COLLEGES

	No.	M	σ	V	Range
Weight..................	499	120.62	15.30	12.68	85 −185
Stature	501	161.60	5.25	3.25	134 −176
Sitting height	366	84.98	2.73	3.21	77.5− 94
Knee height	363	42.10	2.28	5.40	35 − 49
Pubic height	327	77.42	3.85	4.97	67 − 88
Navel height.............	318	96.57	4.26	4.41	84 −109
Sternal height...........	397	132.02	4.71	3.57	120 −146
Girth of head	364	54.73	1.38	2.52	50.5− 60
Girth of neck	373	30.44	1.49	4.90	26.5− 36.5
Girth of chest (N)	413	75.64	4.47	5.91	60.5− 94
Girth of chest (F)	413	81.37	4.27	5.25	72 − 95
Girth of waist...........	413	61.60	4.09	6.64	52 − 80
Girth of hips.............	373	92.33	6.43	6.96	72 −114
Girth of thigh...........	372	54.09	3.06	5.66	41 − 68
Girth of knee	372	34.37	2.57	7.48	26 −46.5
Girth of calf	372	33.25	2.24	6.74	22 − 44
Girth of upper arm	372	25.93	2.25	8.68	21 − 34
Girth of elbow	372	21.56	1.41	6.54	19.5− 26.5
Girth of forearm	372	22.18	1.25	5.64	18 − 26.5
Girth of wrist	372	14.16	.73	5.08	12 − 16.5
Breadth of head	364	14.72	.53	3.60	13 − 16.5
Breadth of neck	368	9.45	.60	6.35	7.5− 11
Breadth of shoulders	372	36.75	1.82	4.95	32 −43.5
Breadth of waist	371	21.40	1.69	7.90	14.5− 26
Breadth of hips	370	33.01	2.45	7.42	23 − 42
Breadth between nipples ...	197	19.86	1.88	9.47	10.5− 27
Shoulder-elbow length	365	33.46	1.34	4.01	29 − 39
Elbow-finger length	361	42.12	1.89	4.49	31.5− 50
Length of foot	364	23.32	1.08	4.63	19.5− 26.5
Span....................	347	162.36	6.45	3.97	146 −183.5

TABLE 112

VARIOUS MEASUREMENTS — DAUGHTERS OF ALL COLLEGES

	No.	M	p.e.	σ	p.e.	V	p.e.	Range
Weight..............	572	124.62	...	15.24	...	12.23	...	86–190
Stature	571	164.53	...	5.47	...	3.33	...	150–180
Sitting height	198	86.77	...	2.80	...	3.23	...	80– 96
Girth of chest (N) ...	253	78.01	...	4.80	...	6.15	...	65– 92
Girth of chest (F)	381	84.91	...	4.44	...	5.23	...	74–100
Girth of waist........	352	65.16	...	4.86	...	7.46	...	51– 86
Girth of hips........	223	93.42	.29	6.50	.21	6.96	.22	77–114
Girth of forearm	137	22.92	.11	1.88	.08	8.20	.34	16– 29
Girth of upper arm ...	137	26.18	.16	2.68	.11	10.24	.42	19– 37
Breadth of shoulders .	162	36.89	.10	1.88	.07	5.10	.19	31– 43
Breadth of waist	155	21.67	.10	1.77	.07	8.17	.31	17– 28
Breadth of hips	29	30.28	.24	1.94	.17	6.41	.57	27– 35

TABLE 113

COMPARISON OF STATISTICAL CONSTANTS OF MOTHERS AND DAUGHTERS —
ALL COLLEGES

	Mothers			Daughters		
	M	σ	V	M	σ	V
Weight................	120.62	15.30	12.68	124.62	15.24	12.23
Stature	161.60	5.25	3.25	164.53	5.47	3.33
Sitting height	84.98	2.73	3.21	86.77	2.80	3.23
Girth of chest (N)	75.64	4.47	5.91	78.01	4.80	6.15
Girth of chest (F)	81.37	4.27	5.25	84.91	4.44	5.23
Girth of waist..........	61.60	4.09	6.64	65.16	4.86	7.46
Girth of hips...........	92.33	6.43	6.96	93.42	6.50	6.96
Girth of forearm	22.18	1.25	6.64	22.92	1.88	8.20
Girth of upper arm	25.93	2.25	8.68	26.18	2.68	10.24
Breadth of shoulders ...	36.75	1.82	4.95	36.89	1.88	5.10
Breadth of waist	21.40	1.69	7.90	21.67	1.77	8.17
Breadth of hips	33.01	2.45	7.42	30.28	1.94	6.41

Stature

The mean stature for the mothers is 161.60, with a standard deviation of 5.25 and a coefficient of variation of 3.25. The mean is considerably above the results of previous authorities for the same period, as shown in Table 114. In the case of the latter measurements the median rather than the mean was used. The numbers are probably sufficiently large, however, to justify their use in comparisons.

TABLE 114

STATURES OF COLLEGE WOMEN — EARLY COMPARATIVE DATA *

College	Years	No.	Age	M	Authority and Date
Wellesley........	1874	1600	19.1	160.5	Wood (1893)
Oberlin	1875	1600	19.3	159.0	Hanna (1894)
Nebraska	1877–86	1500	16–25	160.0	Clapp (1902)

TABLE 115

STATURES OF COLLEGE WOMEN — LATER COMPARATIVE DATA *

College	No.	M	Authority and Date
Smith	100	162.80	Steggerda, Crane, and Steele (1929)
Smith	50	160.48	Davenport and Steggerda (1929)
Smith	100	163.80	Wilder and Pfeiffer (1924)
University of Minnesota	1019	161.69	Jackson (1929)
Hollins	1017	159.65	Palmer (1929)
Vassar	7060	162.40	Newcomer (1921)
Smith	3001	162.47	Richards (1921)

* Jackson (1930), modified from Table 2, p. 368.
The years of birth are computed on the basis of age and date of publication of material.

For the daughters stature is 164.53, showing an increase over the mothers of 2.93 centimeters. The mean stature of the mothers is therefore 97 percent of the daughters' mean stature. This is considerably above the figure given in any of the previously published comparative data. Table 115 shows there is a range from 159.6 to 163.80, but the maximum is .73 centimeters less than that obtained in the present study.

Immediately, however, the question arises as to the value of comparing means of groups whose measurements were taken at different periods. We have seen that in the case of the men the factor of annual increase cannot be ignored, and the same is equally true for the women. This difference, in fact, is absolutely the same as for men, and proportionally even greater, and its influence, if persistent, will tend to decrease the absolute and relative differences in stature between the two sexes. Its operation therefore must be taken into consideration, if anything like accurate comparisons are to be made.

In Table 116 all the women (mothers and daughters) have been classed together and arranged according to years of birth for stature. It will be noticed that the increase has been rather irregular but quite marked.

TABLE 116

STATURE OF FEMALE STUDENTS BY BIRTH DECADES

Years	No.	M	p. e.	σ	p. e.	V	p. e.	Range
1856–65	45	160.9	.59	5.85	.42	3.64	.26	145–175
1866–75	235	160.69	.23	5.13	.16	3.19	.10	148–175
1876–85	212	161.77	.23	4.98	.16	3.08	.10	145–178
1886–95	40	163.30	.58	5.43	.41	3.33	.25	148–175
1896–05	266	163.99	.21	5.19	.15	3.17	.09	148–178
1906–15	267	164.98	.24	5.82	.17	3.53	.10	151–181

In Tables 117 and 118 the differences of stature and the differences in terms of their probable errors are tabulated. In the first decade for which there were sufficient measurements, there was a decrease of .21 centimeters, or an annual decrease of .02 centimeters. The reason for the initial drop is probably the small sample employed, for in succeeding tables the differences follow much the same pattern as for the men, as shown in Table 22. The differences in terms of the probable error show that two of the five differences are significant, two are quite dubious, and the fifth is negative. There is a mean decade figure of 2. The mean annual increase is .08, exactly the same as that for men. On the whole, therefore, the increase is even more significant in the case of the women, since absolute and not comparative differences are concerned. Since the mean annual difference is .08 centimeters or .196 times the probable error, it would take only 15.3 years for a statistically significant difference (3 times the probable error) to occur. If the first decade, for which there is an inadequate sample, were to be omitted, it would take about a decade for the difference to become significant.

TABLE 117

INCREASE FOR STATURE OF FEMALE STUDENTS BY BIRTH DECADES — ALL COLLEGES

Years	1856–65	1866–75	1876–85	1886–95	1896–05
1866–75	−.21	..			
1876–85	.87	1.08	..		
1886–95	2.40	2.61	1.53	..	
1896–05	3.09	3.30	2.22	.69	..
1906–15	4.08	4.29	3.21	1.68	.99
Annual increase	−.02	.12	.15	.07	.10

Mean annual increase .08

TABLE 118

DIFFERENCES IN TERMS OF PROBABLE ERROR FOR STATURE OF FEMALE
STUDENTS BY BIRTH DECADES — ALL COLLEGES

Years	1856–65	1866–75	1876–85	1886–95	1896–05
1866–75	−.33	..			
1876–85	3.00	3.33	..		
1886–95	5.45	5.78	2.45	..	
1896–05	6.57	6.90	3.57	1.12	..
1906–15	9.70	10.03	6.70	4.25	3.13

Mean decade figure 1.96

TABLE 119

STATURE OF FEMALE JAPANESE *

Years	No.	Age	M	Authority
1879	16	17–42	143.00	Ayrton
1888	100	...	145.58	Sakaki
1889	12	...	145.16	Soller
1901	316	18–40	146.45	Miwa
1901	760	...	146.50	Ogata
....	762	18–40	146.60	Nippon Life Insurance Company
1925	1200	Adults	149.92	Matsumura

* Annual Report of the Educational Department of Japan (after Matsumura).

TABLE 120

MEAN STATURE OF FEMALE JAPANESE STUDENTS AGED 18–30 (1909–18)*

Years	No.	M
1909	3706	148.18
1910	3959	148.53
1911	4762	149.50
1912	5320	149.74
1913	5397	149.53
1914	5469	149.32
1915	5196	149.23
1916	5018	149.02
1917	4671	149.77
1918	4563	149.23

Increase 1.06   Annual increase .106

* The Annual Report of the Educational Department of Japan (after Matsumura).

Hrdlička [1] has stated that there has been an increase of one inch in the past thirty years, and Jackson [2] takes this into consideration when he compares the Minnesota women with the Nebraska, Wellesley, and Oberlin material (Table 114). Actually, however, the increase would appear to be 2.40 centimeters or slightly less. There has been marked increase in Japanese women (Table 119).

Weight

In weight the mean of the entire series for mothers is 120.62 pounds, and for daughters 124.62 pounds, showing a difference in favor of the daughters of 4.00 pounds. The mean weight of the mothers represents 97 percent of that of the daughters (Table 126).

The same general tendency is apparent as in the case of stature, but to a less marked degree. This is to be expected, inasmuch as there has not been an increase in weight comparable with the increase in stature. The women have become taller and, proportionally but not absolutely, more slender.

The mothers are in every case heavier than women of the same general period on the basis of comparative data as shown in Table 121.

TABLE 121

WEIGHTS OF COLLEGE WOMEN — EARLY COMPARATIVE DATA *

College	No.	Years	Weight	Author and Date
Wellesley	1600	1874	117.28	Wood 1893
Oberlin	1600	1875	112.43	Hanna 1894
Nebraska............	1500	1877–86	113.31	Clapp 1902

* Age in each case is approximately 19.

The daughters likewise are heavier than women of the same general period. It must be remembered, however, that even in a few years the weight increase might be sufficient to affect significantly the comparisons.

The following table gives comparative data from various colleges at approximately the same periods.

The unweighted mean for the Minnesota, Wisconsin, Stanford, and Vassar women is 122 pounds, or somewhat less than the mean for the daughters of the present study, but considerably above the average of 114.6 pounds found by Sargent (1889).

[1] 1925.   [2] 1930, pp. 371-372.

Arranged by decades according to years of birth, the results are similar to those obtained for stature (see Tables 116 and 123). The mean annual increase, as noted in Table 124, is .10 pounds, with a range from .02 to .20 pounds. On the basis of the annual increase, it would consequently take 34.09 years for a significant increase to occur, since the mean figure for the difference in terms of the probable error for each decade is .88.

TABLE 122

WEIGHTS OF COLLEGE WOMEN — LATER COMPARATIVE DATA

College	No.	Years	Weight	Author and Date *
Minnesota	1022	1905	119.61	Jackson 1926
Wisconsin	1106	1907	120.96	Bardeen 1927
Stanford	430	1895–08	120.65	Passmore and Weymouth 1924
Vassar	1233	....	123.33	Newcomer 1921 (Entrants 1916–20)
Vassar	296	....	124.43	Newcomer 1921 (Entrants 1920)

* Jackson (1930), p. 374.

TABLE 123

WEIGHT OF FEMALE STUDENTS BY BIRTH DECADES — ALL COLLEGES

Years	No.	M	p. e.	σ	p. e.	V	p. e.	Range
1856–65	43	119.88	1.43	13.90	1.01	11.60	.85	85–153
1866–75	235	120.45	.65	14.70	.46	12.21	.38	85–185
1876–85	212	120.70	.74	16.10	.53	13.34	.44	80–180
1886–95	40	121.65	1.43	13.40	1.01	11.02	.83	80–160
1896–05	266	123.70	.62	15.15	.44	12.25	.36	90–180
1906–15	267	125.25	.67	16.45	.48	13.13	.38	75–190

TABLE 124

INCREASE OF WEIGHT FOR FEMALE STUDENTS BY BIRTH DECADES — ALL COLLEGES

Years	1856–65	1866–75	1876–85	1886–95	1896–05
1866–75	.57	..			
1876–85	.82	.25	..		
1886–95	1.77	1.20	.95	..	
1896–05	3.82	3.25	3.00	2.05	..
1906–15	5.37	4.80	4.55	3.60	1.55
Annual increase	.06	.02	.09	.20	.15
Mean annual increase .10					

TABLE 125

DIFFERENCES IN TERMS OF PROBABLE ERROR FOR WEIGHT OF FEMALE
STUDENTS BY BIRTH DECADES — ALL COLLEGES

Years	1856–65	1866–75	1876–85	1886–95	1896–05
1866–75	.35	..			
1876–85	.61	.25	..		
1886–95	1.19	.83	.58	..	
1896–05	2.51	2.15	1.90	1.32	..
1906–15	4.41	4.05	3.80	3.22	1.90

Mean decade figure .88

We have already observed that in the case of stature it would take 15.3 years for a significant difference to occur. In comparison with weight, therefore, it would appear that it would take approximately twice the length of time for a similarly important change to take place.

In summary, we may conclude that weight is increasing similarly to stature, and the data for women thus confirms that obtained for men, showing clearly that the same general changes obtain for both sexes.

Sitting Height

The sitting height of the daughters is considerably above that of the mothers; the former, with a mean of 86.77, and the latter, with one of 84.98, show a difference of 1.79 centimeters. The daughters are decidedly longer in the trunk than the women of Minnesota University (Jackson), whose sitting height is 84.35.

The relative sitting heights show that the daughters with 52.74 approach closer to the normal index for European women (53) as determined by Martin [1] than the mothers with an index of 52.59. It would appear that the trunk measurements of the daughters are increasing proportionately more than the stature. This is the reverse of the situation noticed in the men's series, where the relative height decreased considerably. At Minnesota the relative sitting height was 52.2 (Jackson), at Wisconsin 53 (Bardeen), at Stanford (Passmore and Weymouth) 52.8, at Smith (Wilder and Pfeiffer) 52.8, at Wellesley (Wood) 52.7, and at Oberlin (Hanna) 52.9.

---

[1] 1928, p. 339.

The only comparable data for the mothers in America, so far as period of measurement is concerned, is from Nebraska (Clapp), where the index was 53.2, slightly in excess of the European average for women, and considerably greater than that of the present series. Since the stature of the Nebraska women was only 160, however, this is in accordance with the scale of 52.8 for statures of 159–160 and 52.5 for statures of 162 as given by Martin.[1] Hrdlička gives the sitting height of Old Americans (age 41) as 87.27 and the relative sitting height as 53.92. The age is probably accountable for the difference.

Girth of Chest (N)

The chest measurements show that the daughters are considerably more developed than the mothers as regards lung capacity and girth.

In girth of chest at rest, or what is designated "normal girth," the difference is 2.37 centimeters, the mothers measuring 72.64 and the daughters 78.01 centimeters, the percent being 97. The latter measurement is slightly under that of Minnesota women (Jackson), whose mean is 79.00 centimeters, but the difference is not statistically significant.

Girth of Chest (F)

The girth of chest full is even greater in the daughters over their mothers than the chest normal. The difference, 3.54 centimeters, shows that the lung capacity has decidedly increased, the mean for the former being 5.73 and for the latter 6.90 centimeters. Jackson found the expansion among Minnesota girls was 6.37 centimeters.

The increase in expansion and capacity shows the effects of the relief of pressure on the thoracic region. There can be no doubt but that the wasp-waists of the mothers materially affected breathing, and the relief from this pressure in the daughters has shown the extent of the handicap imposed upon the women of thirty years ago.

Girth of Waist

In girth of waist there is an excess on the part of the daughters of 3.56 centimeters, the means for mothers and daughters being respectively 61.60 and 65.16 centimeters. The mothers represent 94 percent of the daughters. The great difference is probably largely

[1] *Ibid.*, p. 337.

to be accounted for by the change in fashion and the freedom from the constrictive clothing worn by the mothers.

In proportion to breadth of waist the results are somewhat more difficult to explain. The daughters show an increase of only .27 centimeters. It would seem, therefore, that abdominal development is somewhat greater proportionally among the daughters than among the mothers. Whether or not there is any correlation between the changes in waist measurements and those in hip measurements is problematical.

Girth of Hips

Although, as in the case of girth of waist, there is an excess in girth of hips on the part of the daughters, the increase is not as great. The significance of the difference is not wholly clear, but it is probably due to change in fashion and the consequent change in pressure in the region of the hips. The mean for the mothers is 92.33 centimeters, for the daughters 93.42 centimeters, with a difference of 1.09 centimeters, the mothers representing 99 percent of the daughters' measurement.

Girth of Forearm

Girth of forearm shows proportionally rather a high percentile increase, the mothers representing only 97 percent of the daughters' measurements. The means are respectively 22.18 and 22.92 centimeters. The difference, .74 centimeters, shows considerable development of daughters over mothers.

Girth of Upper Arm

In comparison with the forearm there is both proportionally and absolutely less increase on the part of daughters over mothers. The mean for the former is 26.18, for the latter 25.93, with a difference of .25 centimeters, the mothers representing 99 percent of the daughters' measurement. This is the reverse of what might normally be expected, for it would seem more likely that greater increase should occur in the upper arm rather than in the forearm.

Breadth of Shoulders

In measurements which depend largely on the skeletal frame, e. g. breadth of shoulders, hips, stature, length of arm, etcetera, the variability due to the constrictive effects of tight clothing is far less noticeable than in the case of those measurements which are made on the softer regions of the body, such as the girth of the waist, calf, chest, etcetera.

In shoulder breadth this is particularly noticeable. The means of the mothers and daughters, 36.75 and 36.89 respectively, are nearly equal, with a difference of only .14 centimeters. This is considerably less, however, than the difference between the two generations in breadth of hips. It would seem, therefore, that the women are increasing in breadth of hips far more than in breadth of shoulders or breadth of waist. There is in fact a general progression in increase of difference from shoulders through waist and hips.

Breadth of Waist

The mothers are only slightly narrower (.27 centimeters) in breadth of waist than daughters. The mean for the former is 21.40 and for the latter 21.67. The percentile relation of the mothers to the daughters is 99. The significance of this measurement is discussed in connection with girth of waist.

Breadth of Hips

The breadth of hips in the mothers is 33.01 centimeters, and in the daughters 30.28 centimeters, showing a difference in favor of the mothers of 2.73 centimeters. This is considerably above the figures of Bach [1] for German women, where the mean is 29.40 centimeters for statures of 162 centimeters and 29.7 for statures of 165 centimeters. It would appear that American women had rather broad hips, but that these are getting considerably narrower. The small series of daughters is hardly large enough, however, to permit any definite conclusions.

A comparison of girths, as already indicated, shows an increase in circumference on the part of the daughters, despite an accompanying decrease in breadth. The only possible explanation for such a condition seems to be that the general body build has changed and that there is a greater increase in the region of the buttocks.

UNIT DIFFERENCES AND PERCENTILE RELATIONSHIP

In actual unit differences, daughters show increases over their mothers in all measurements except breadth of hips (Table 126). In stature, the actual increase of 2.93 centimeters may be taken as

[1] Martin (1928), p. 353.

the mean difference of the present generation over the past, and represents an accumulation of the annual increase noted throughout the population as a whole. The same explanation must be made, therefore, as in the case of the male students, i. e. that the increase is due not to any hereditary change from within, but rather to some factor from without. In other words, it is not because the daughters are daughters that they are taller, but because they were born thirty years or so later.

In other measurements the increases are quite varied and can best be expressed on the percentage basis. The highest percentage is in breadth of hips. In this instance, where the mothers considerably exceed the daughters, the difference is greatly in favor of the former. In fact in all three breadth measurements the percentage runs high, with a mean of 102.85 percent. In all the other measurements or groups of measurements the percentages are below 100 percent, showing that the daughters in the respective traits are in excess of the mothers.

The most striking differences are in the comparison of breadth of waist and girth of waist with breadth of hips and girth of hips. The differences in percent between the first two mentioned is 4.75. In the case of the last two it is 9.65. This shows that the hips have become considerably narrower in proportion to the girth than has the waist.

TABLE 126

Unit Differences between Mothers and Daughters for Various Measurements — All Colleges *

	Difference	Percent (Daughters = 100)
Weight	4.00	97
Stature	2.93	98
Sitting height	1.79	98
Girth of chest (N)	2.37	97
Girth of chest (F)	3.54	96
Girth of waist	3.56	94
Girth of hips	1.09	99
Girth of forearm	.74	97
Girth of upper arm	.25	99
Breadth of shoulders	.14	99
Breadth of waist	.27	99
Breadth of hips	−2.73	109

* Calculated from the seriation tables.

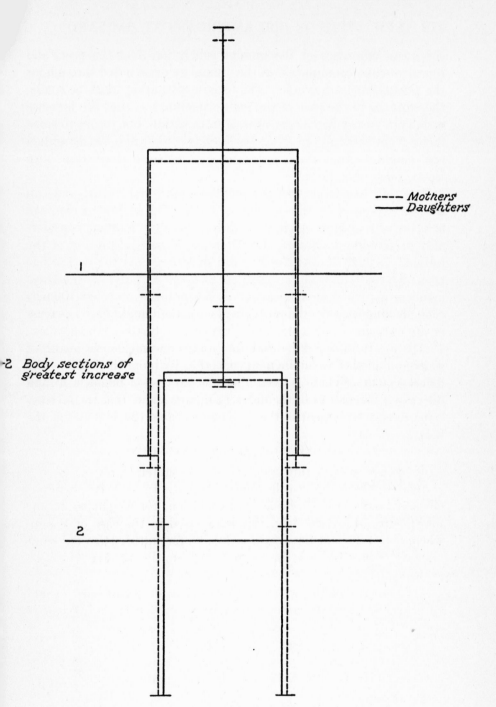

FIG. 14. Increases of various body parts of daughters over mothers

Grouped according to types of measurements, Table 127 shows that in breadths the daughters exceed the mothers least. It would seem, therefore, that the daughters had grown proportionally taller than broader, i. e. that height and length have increased to the sacrifice of breadth.

TABLE 127

PERCENTAGES OF MOTHERS' MEASUREMENTS TO DAUGHTERS' GROUPED
ACCORDING TO TYPE — ALL COLLEGES

	Percent
Weight	97.00
Heights and lengths	98.00
Girths	96.94
Breadths	102.85
Total	98.47

In summary, the original tendency for the daughters to increase in weight, girths, heights, and breadths is further strengthened. It appears from our data that the younger women have increased in general girth measurements proportionally more than in breadth measurements. There is even a loss in the case of breadth of hips. The mean percentage of the different factors shows that the mothers represent 98.47 percent of the daughters (Table 127).

COEFFICIENTS OF CORRELATION

In weight and stature mothers and daughters show far greater correlation than in any other measurement. In both cases the co-efficient is .36. For Wellesley the coefficient for weight is .44 and for stature .31. Peculiarly, this is reversed in the case of Vassar, where the coefficient for weight is .30 and for stature .45. The same reversal occurs likewise in the case of Smith and Mt. Holyoke, showing that there is very great variability.

Figures 15 and 16 show the correlations for stature and weight of mothers and daughters of Wellesley College. Stature is far more irregular than weight, contrary to what might be expected, since the coefficient of the latter is slightly in excess of the former.

The correlation of stature between mothers and daughters, as already noted, is as variable as that of weight, and the weighted mean, .36, is the same.

Sitting height, although not showing as high a coefficient of correlation as stature, is nevertheless appreciably above that of most of the girth and breadth coefficients. There is a progressive lack of correlation from the weight and height measurements through the girth and breadth measurements, as in the case of the men. The tendency is in some cases accentuated by fashion, which has little effect on stature, weight, and shoulder breadths, the more constant measurements.

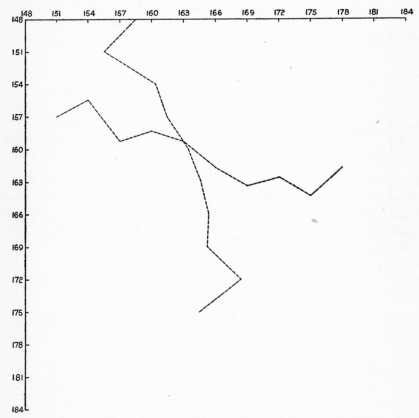

Fig. 15. Correlation between Wellesley mothers and daughters for stature *

* Mothers' measurements on the vertical column.

The coefficients of correlation for girths present some interesting comparisons. From the difference between the coefficients for normal and full chest girths it would appear that the higher correlation in the case of the latter was due not so much to greater similarity as to the fact that the chest expansion was somewhat less in the case of the daughters. In waist measurements the coefficients are appreciably higher than those for the hips. This is to be expected in view of the differences between breadths and circumferences noted above, and is also in keeping with the coefficients for breadth of waist and breadth of hips given below. The coefficient for girth of neck, .12, is very low, and is possibly due to the fashion of high collars among the mothers. In the case of the coefficients for arm girths, where fashion plays little if any part, the correlations are fairly high.

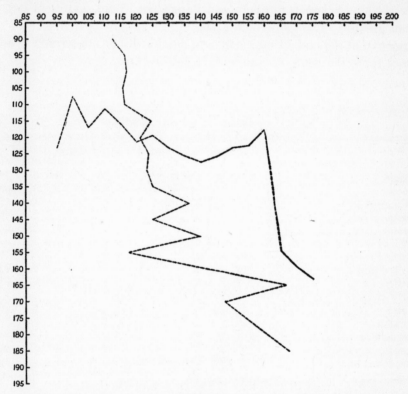

Fig. 16. Correlation between Wellesley mothers and daughters for weight

There is least correlation between breadth measurements, the coefficient in the case of the waist, .10, being the lowest of all the measurements. This again, as in the case of girth of neck, is probably a result of change of fashion. The highest correlation, as might be expected, is noted in the case of breadth of shoulders. This shows that where the body is less adaptable to change by pressure the correlations are higher.

We may conclude that mothers and daughters show greatest similarity in the measurements for weight and stature, slightly less for girths, and least for breadths. The causes are probably twofold: the general increase in stature and proportional lengthening out on the part of the daughters; the fact that fashions have changed and that the various parts of the body which were formerly subjected to pressure, such as the waist, hips, and neck, are allowed to assume their normal proportions. Had fashion dictated a continuance of abnormal restrictions in growth in the softer regions, the correlations between mothers and daughters would doubtless have been greater. The value of the above correlations is therefore to a large extent dependent on mode, and can hardly be considered as an exact representation of the normal relationships.

TABLE 128

COEFFICIENTS OF CORRELATION FOR VARIOUS MEASUREMENTS OF MOTHERS AND DAUGHTERS — VARIOUS COLLEGES

	Wellesley			Vassar			Smith			Mt. Holyoke			Total	
	No.	r	p.e.	No.	r	p.e.	No.	r	p.e.	No.	r	p.e.	No.	r
Weight........	241	.44	.03	229	.30	.04	60	.18	.08	40	.53	.08	570	.36
Stature	241	.31	.04	228	.45	.04	62	.39	.07	40	.19	.10	571	.36
Sitting height .	44	.19	.10	148	.33	.05	..	..	..	..	..	..	192	.29
Girth of chest (N)	24	.34	.12	229	.14	.04	..	..	..	..	..	..	253	.16
Girth of chest (F)	152	.25	.05	229	.27	.04	..	..	..	..	..	..	381	.26
Girth of waist..	131	.25	.06	221	.20	.04	..	..	..	..	..	..	352	.22
Girth of neck ..	..	..	..	160	.18	.05	..	..	..	..	..	..	160	.18
Girth of hips...	..	..	..	223	.12	.04	..	..	..	..	..	..	223	.12
Girth of forearm	..	..	..	137	.32	.05	..	..	..	..	..	..	137	.32
Girth of upper arm	..	..	..	137	.26	.05	..	..	..	..	..	..	137	.26
Breadth of shoulders ...	..	..	..	162	.28	.05	..	..	..	..	..	..	162	.28
Breadth of waist	..	..	..	155	.10	.05	..	..	..	..	..	..	155	.10
Breadth of hips	..	..	..	29	.18	.12	..	..	..	..	..	..	29	.18

Separate Cross-correlation of Mothers and Daughters

In every college there is a higher correlation between stature and weight of mothers than of daughters. The weighted mean coefficient of correlation for the mothers is .51, for the daughters .45 (Table 129). Wellesley shows the highest correlations and Smith the least. In the case of Vassar the mothers and daughters are practically identical, showing coefficients respectively of 52 and 51. The result in the case of the daughters is identical with that found by Jackson for Minnesota girls, .45. The coefficient was .358 in the Swarthmore women measured by Baldwin over a period of four consecutive years. The results are considerably lower than for

TABLE 129

COEFFICIENTS OF CORRELATION OF STATURE AND WEIGHT OF MOTHERS AND
DAUGHTERS CROSS-CORRELATED — VARIOUS COLLEGES

	Wellesley			Vassar			Smith			Mt. Holyoke			Total	
	No.	r	p. e.	No.	r	p. e.	No.	r	p. e.	No.	r	p. e.	No.	r
Mothers......	205	.52	.03	207	.52	.03	51	.46	.07	35	.51	.08	498	.51
Daughters ...	240	.43	.04	229	.51	.03	62	.31	.08	40	.41	.09	571	.45

Europe, and appreciably below those of a generation ago among Old
Americans.

In Figures 17 and 18 the diagram for the correlation between
weight and stature is given separately for Wellesley College mothers

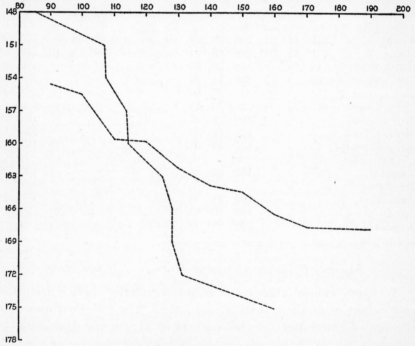

FIG. 17. Correlation between weight and stature for Wellesley mothers

and daughters. Both coefficients are fairly high, .52 and .43 respectively. They are also quite regular, and far more uniform than
the correlation for stature or weight correlated separately between
mothers and daughters.

INDICES

Comparisons between mothers and daughters can hardly be
drawn on the basis of the three indices available from both series.
In each case, however, the figures are in favor of the daughters, and

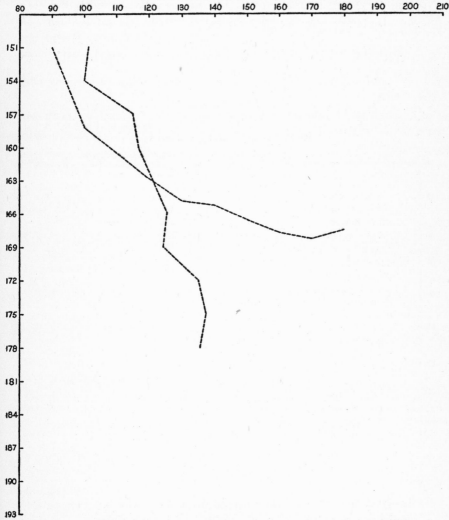

FIG. 18. Correlation between weight and stature for Wellesley daughters

may thus be somewhat significant. In the case of the mothers, the
indices are all in general accord with figures given by Martin for
German women, although there is a tendency on the part of the

mothers to run higher indices in the length measurements and less in the breadths and girths.

Relative navel height is the same as that given by Martin, 59.7 for Norwegians and for Europeans at large. The relative shoulder breadth is slightly greater than that of Europeans, who average 22.2. No comparative data are available for relative breadth between nipples and for sternal height. Relative sitting height is discussed under sitting height. Relative foot length is the same as Hrdlička's figure for Old Americans, 14.42, and considerably less than the English material (15.36) cited by him.

TABLE 130

Various Measurements of Mothers and Daughters in Proportion to Stature — All Colleges

	Mothers	Daughters
Span	100.05	
Navel height	59.76	
Sitting height	52.59	52.74
Pubic height	47.91	
Sternal height	81.70	
Trunk	33.79	
Upper arm	20.71	
Elbow-fingertip length	26.06	
Knee height	26.05	
Foot length	14.43	
Breadth between nipples	12.29	
Breadth of hips	20.43	
Breadth of shoulders	22.74	
Girth of chest (N)	46.81	47.41
Girth of thigh	33.47	
Girth of waist	38.12	39.60
Girth of hips	57.14	
Other Indices		
Upper arm length — Elbow-fingertip length	79.44	
Girth of upper arm — Girth of thigh	47.94	

EYE COLOR

Observations on eye color are limited to mothers. The figures are computed from the original records, and must therefore be considered as of little value scientifically. The data are not comparable with Hrdlička's Old American material. Undoubtedly the larger percentage of those designated as blue were in reality mixed. The same is probably true of the brown, for both of the categories are disproportionately large. Table 131 shows the frequencies of the different colors and their percentages for the 162 observations recorded.

TABLE 131

EYE COLOR — WELLESLEY COLLEGE MOTHERS (162)

	Light Blue	Blue	Gray	Hazel	Brown	Black
No.	1	67	27	6	58	3

	Blue	Gray	Dark
No.	68	27	67
Percent	41.9	16.6	41.3

SISTERS

In the case of the brothers, increase in stature and weight with successive juniority was noted. For sisters the data, although not as ample, are even more interesting as regards this phenomenon. In Table 132 are listed the statistical constants for weight and stature of the first-born, second-born, and third-born sisters. Here, as with the brothers, the term first-born or second-born refers merely to the order of precedence, and does not indicate the actual sequence of births in a given family. There is no cognizance taken of the brothers, the children who died in infancy and childhood, or the sisters who failed to matriculate at college. The ages are approximately 17 years for all sets of sisters.

TABLE 132

COMPARISON OF WEIGHT AND STATURE OF SISTERS BY SENIORITY OF BIRTH — ALL COLLEGES

	No.	M	p.e.	σ	p.e.	Range
Stature						
First	70	163.93	.40	4.89	.28	157–178
Second	70	164.47	.48	5.91	.34	151–178
Third	7	166.63	1.46	5.73	1.03	163–181
Weight						
First	70	124.20	1.15	14.15	.81	95–165
Second	70	125.15	1.30	16.05	.91	100–190
Third	7	128.95	4.60	18.05	1.03	110–165

Again, as with the brothers, the differences progressively increase: for weight from .95 centimeters, between first-born and second-born, to 3.80 centimeters between second-born and third-born; and from .54 centimeters to 2.16 for stature. The differences and differences in terms of their probable errors are given in Tables 133–136.

TABLE 133

INCREASE IN WEIGHT OF OLDER AND YOUNGER SISTERS — ALL COLLEGES

	First Sister	Second Sister
Second sister......................	.95	..
Third sister	4.75	3.80

TABLE 134

DIFFERENCES IN WEIGHT OF OLDER AND YOUNGER SISTERS IN TERMS OF PROBABLE ERROR — ALL COLLEGES

	First Sister	Second Sister
Second sister......................	.55	..
Third sister	1.00	.79

TABLE 135

INCREASE IN STATURE OF OLDER AND YOUNGER SISTERS — ALL COLLEGES

	First Sister	Second Sister
Second sister......................	.54	..
Third sister	2.70	2.16

TABLE 136

DIFFERENCES FOR STATURE OF OLDER AND YOUNGER SISTERS IN TERMS OF PROBABLE ERROR — ALL COLLEGES

	First Sister	Second Sister
Second sister......................	.88	..
Third sister	1.79	1.41

Comparatively small samples, especially in the third group, make the value of the tables less than in the case of the brothers. The sisters' measurements, however, confirm those of the brothers, and seem to show fairly conclusively that there must be some factor other than chance which manifests with such consistent regularity the observed tendency toward physical increment.

There is no correction for annual increase, since its occurrence, although it materially influences the results, does not change the fact of the increase. Even if the correction were introduced it would not prevent the ultimate conclusion that younger sisters are taller than older sisters, for younger sisters are of necessity born at a later date.

The coefficient of correlation for weight, .71, is surprisingly high, and nearly twice that for stature, .38 (Table 137). On the basis of the correlation table, the differences of the means for weight and stature are respectively 1.35 pounds and .89 centimeter (Table 138). In Figures 19 and 20 the correlations are graphically illustrated.

TABLE 137

COEFFICIENTS OF CORRELATION OF WEIGHT AND STATURE OF OLDER AND YOUNGER SISTERS — ALL COLLEGES

	No.	r	p. e.
Weight..........................	77	.71	.04
Stature	77	.38	.07
Mean	77	.55	

TABLE 138

UNIT DIFFERENCES BETWEEN OLDER AND YOUNGER SISTERS — ALL COLLEGES

	Difference	Percent (Younger Sisters = 100)
Weight......................	1.35	99.
Stature	.89	99.4

The percentile relations show that the younger sisters get proportionally taller rather than heavier, although in both stature and weight the absolute measurements are in favor of the younger sisters. The percentages of older to younger sisters in stature and weight are respectively 99.4 and 99 (Table 138).

The means for stature calculated from Pearson's data on sisters (Table 139) shows that there is a difference of .38 centimeters, or 3.36 times the probable error. It is quite apparent, therefore, that the difference is statistically significant. Even assuming that the mean age seniority difference between the sisters was four years, and allowing consequently .32 centimeters, or four times the mean annual increase of .08, the result thus corrected would still be fairly significant, although hardly enough so to justify any definite conclusions.

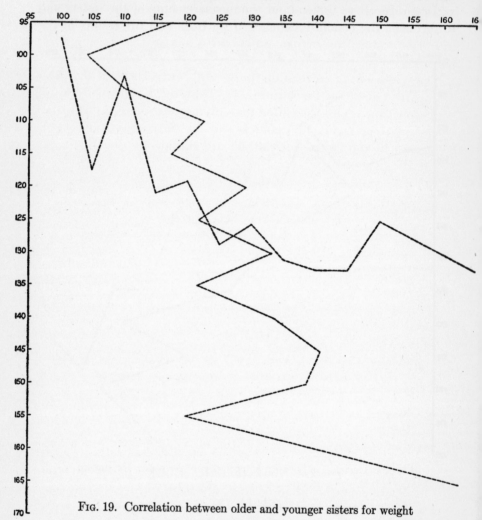

Fig. 19. Correlation between older and younger sisters for weight

Boas has found contradictory evidence for sisters as well as for brothers. For sisters the data on stature is far more irregular than for brothers. The differences from the mean between the ages of 6.5 and 18 are shown in Table 140.[1] Grouped according to older and

[1] It is impossible to correct for annual increase in view of the fact that the age difference cannot be determined.

younger sisters there is a difference of one centimeter. For sisters 16.5 years old, the same age as selected for the boys, the progression is the reverse of that in the brothers. In weight the results are less significant, although the same general tendency is present.

It is difficult to understand the measurements of the sisters and to reconcile the conclusions reached by Boas and the results of the

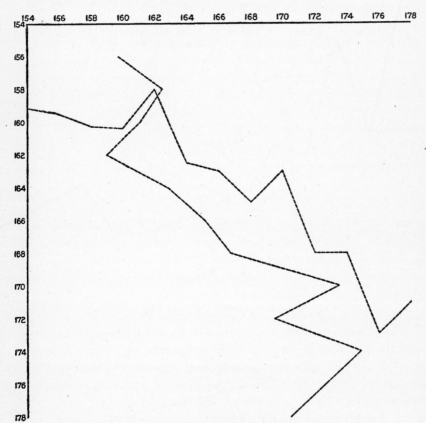

Fig. 20. Correlation between older and younger sisters for stature

TABLE 139

COMPARISON OF STATURE OF OLDER AND YOUNGER SISTERS BASED ON PEARSON'S MATERIAL *

	No.	M	p. e.	σ	p. e.	V	p. e.	Range
Older sisters	473	162.23	.08	2.71	.06	4.24	.09	132.08–188
Younger sisters ..	473	162.61	.08	2.57	.06	4.01	.09	139.7 –182.88

* Calculated from Table lxi, Pearson and Lee (1903), p. 446.

present study. Until more evidence is available the exact nature, extent, and direction of increase as regards precedence in age probably cannot be determined. It would certainly appear, however, that the same factors are operating in the women as in the men, and in the former to a more marked degree than in the latter.

TABLE 140

DIFFERENCES BETWEEN AVERAGE STATURE FOR SISTERS AND STATURE ACCORDING TO BIRTH (BOAS *)

Age	First-born	Second-born	Third-born	Fourth-born	Later-born
6.5–18	.71	−.28	−.45	−.33	−.23

* 1895.

TABLE 141

DIFFERENCES BETWEEN AVERAGE STATURE OF BROTHERS AND SISTERS AND STATURE ACCORDING TO BIRTH (BOAS)

Age	No.	First-born	Second-born	Third-born	Fourth-born	Later-born
16.5	127	+15	−38	−3	−1	−18

CONCLUSIONS

PARENTAL RESEMBLANCE AND ALTERATION IN TYPE

The present generation of female students shows actual increases over the previous generation in all measurements except breadth of hips. From our data the same general changes are indicated as for the males. There is an annual increase in stature throughout the female population as a whole of .08 centimeters, exactly the same as for the men and proportionally even greater. The same conclusion can be drawn, then, as in the case of the male students — that the increase is due not to any hereditary change but rather to some factor or to multiple factors from without. Stature increases significantly every 15.3 years, and weight, which shows the same tendencies to a less marked degree, increases significantly every 34 years.

Proportionally the daughters, although heavier and taller, are more slender, since the breadth measurements have increased very slightly (with an actual decrease in breadth of hips) in proportion to height and girth measurements. The relative sitting height shows that the females are increasing more in trunk length in proportion to stature, the reverse of the situation in the males. In general the measurements which depend on the skeletal frame, i. e. breadths, are much less variable than those on the softer parts of the body, i. e. girths, where the tight clothing worn by the past generation had marked constrictive effect. Thus differences in body build of the daughters are due partly to actual elongation and proportional narrowing, and partly, perhaps, to the effects of change in fashion.

Degree of parental resemblance for mothers and daughters is about ¼ to 1, approximately the same as for men. The average coefficient of correlation for all measurements is only .24, as opposed to an average of .46 by Pearson [1] for mothers and daughters.

Sororal Resemblance

The general inheritance pattern for sisters is much the same as for brothers. Pearson [2] found a coefficient of correlation of .54 in stature, as opposed to .71 in the present study. In weight the coefficient of the present study is .38. The difference is probably largely to be accounted for on the basis of the rather fragmentary sample. The mean for the three characters of stature, span, and forearm given by Pearson is .533 and is in sensible agreement with the mean of stature and weight, .55, of the present series.

The significance of the data on sisters may be summarized as follows. (1) Increase is apparent in both stature and weight with each successive sister; (2) the increase is not altogether accountable on the basis of annual increase, but is due also to other contributory factors; (3) the results are essentially the same as for brothers, and tend to substantiate the conclusions reached regarding them; (4) the significance of measurements in regard to adolescence is more obscure than in the case of boys, but this may be due to the greater variability on the part of women as a whole; (5) stature and weight are inherited in unequal degrees, but roughly the mean coefficient for inheritance of the two measurements would be about .55.

[1] Pearson and Lee (1903), p. 378.
[2] Pearson and Lee (1903), p. 387.

Chapter IV

RESULTS OF THE STUDY OF NEW PHYSICAL TYPES

MALE AND FEMALE STUDENTS COMPARED

THE present data include the small series of men, and all of the women's series. The purpose of the comparison is to determine the degrees of changes in bodily measurements in the two sexes, and the varying tendencies exhibited.

The ages, although not the same, ranging in means for the four groups (father, son, mother, daughter) from 17 to 19, are nevertheless comparable, inasmuch as age differences are not statistically significant among students. The generation difference of about thirty-five years is a convenient period interval, and is therefore used for sexual comparisons; the results are applicable to any period of thirty-five years for student groups.

In Table 142 are listed the means for fathers and mothers and the percentile relations. These may be considered as the general proportions of male and female students measured in the nineteenth year in the last decade of the nineteenth century.

In almost every instance the men are sensibly larger than the women, particularly in weight, lengths, and thoracic measurements. The only measurements in which the women are actually larger are girth of hips and girth of thigh, but they approach the men very closely in breadth of hips. They are clearly inferior in girths of the arm, chest, waist, and neck, and also in most breadth measurements. The lowest percentages are those for breadth and girth of waist and for weight.

We may therefore conclude that the women had proportionally very small waists but large hips, small chests and arms, and rather big legs. In stature they were more nearly the equal of males than in weight. For data a generation later we are less fortunate.

Only a very few measurements were taken on the daughters; consequently it is more difficult to get a comparative idea of the male and female of the present day. In Table 143 the percentages of mothers to fathers and sons to daughters are compared for such measurements as are available for all four groups. In the table the two groups are designated respectively thirty-five years ago and today.

Plainly in almost every category the women have become proportionally smaller. In weight there is a pronounced drop of over 3 percent, whereas stature has remained about the same. The most signal change is in the hip measurements. Whereas the older genera-

TABLE 142

MEANS OF FATHERS AND MOTHERS AND PERCENT OF MOTHERS' TO FATHERS' MEASUREMENTS

	Fathers	Mothers	Percent (Fathers = 100)
Weight......................	140.24	120.62	86.0
Stature	173.95	161.60	92.9
Sitting height	90.95	84.98	94.3
Knee height	46.66	42.10	90.2
Pubic height	87.10	77.42	88.9
Navel height................	103.72	96.57	93.1
Sternal height..............	141.83	132.02	93.1
Girth of head	..	54.73	..
Girth of neck	34.70	30.44	87.8
Girth of chest (N)	86.88	75.64	87.
Girth of chest (F)	91.88	81.37	88.5
Girth of waist..............	72.88	61.60	84.5
Girth of hips...............	89.28	92.33	103.4
Girth of thigh..............	52.12	54.09	103.8
Girth of knee	35.52	34.37	96.8
Girth of calf	35.09	35.25	94.7
Girth of upper arm	29.37	25.93	88.2
Girth of elbow	25.17	21.56	85.6
Girth of forearm	25.78	22.18	86.0
Girth of wrist	16.23	14.16	87.4
Breadth of head	153.00 *	147.2	96.2
Breadth of neck	10.94	9.45	86.7
Breadth of shoulders	42.69	36.75	86.1
Breadth of waist	25.33	21.40	84.6
Breadth of hips	33.06	33.01	99.7
Breadth between nipples	20.26	19.86	97.8
Shoulder-elbow length	37.55	33.46	89.2
Elbow-finger length	46.92	42.12	89.8
Length of foot	25.98	23.32	89.7
Span.......................	178.20	162.36	91.1

* Millimeters.

tion showed such marked differences as 103.40 in girth and 99.70 in breadth, the present generation women have dropped to 101.80 and 92.00 respectively, differences of −1.60 percent and −7.70 percent. It thus appears that women have become proportionally narrower in the hips but have retained most of the girth. The same is true for the men in possibly an even more marked degree.

In waist measurements the opposite applies. The women have become proportionally larger in girth, but have remained essentially

TABLE 143

COMPARISON OF PERCENTAGES OF FEMALE TO MALE MEASUREMENTS OF STUDENTS BY GENERATION

	35 Years Ago Percent	Today Percent	Difference
Weight......................	86.00	82.90	−3.10
Stature	92.90	92.70	−.20
Sitting height	94.30	94.20	−.10
Girth of chest (N)	87.00	85.80	−1.20
Girth of chest (F)	88.50	90.00	1.50
Girth of waist...............	84.50	88.70	4.20
Girth of hips................	103.40	101.80	−1.60
Girth of upper arm	88.20	85.00	−3.20
Girth of forearm	85.60	85.50	−.10
Breadth of shoulders	86.10	84.40	−1.70
Breadth of waist	84.60	83.70	−.90
Breadth of hips	99.70	92.00	−7.70
Total mean	90.10	88.90	−1.20

TABLE 144

PERCENTAGES OF FEMALE TO MALE MEASUREMENTS GROUPED BY TYPE OF STUDENTS BY GENERATION

	35 Years Ago Percent	Today Percent	Difference
Weight......................	86.00	82.90	−3.10
Heights and lengths	93.60	93.45	−.15
Girths	89.60	89.50	−.10
Breadths	91.10	86.70	−4.40
Weighted mean	90.10	88.90	
Difference...................	...	...	−1.20

the same in breadth. In chest measurements the expansion has increased more in women than in men, and the proportional sitting heights have remained practically constant. In order to condense the measurements for further comparison they are grouped according to types in Table 144.

It is apparent that there are certain differences of more than casual significance. The greatest changes have occurred in breadths and weight and least in girths and heights and lengths. Had the fashion of constricting the waist continued the difference in girths would probably be more marked; the percentages are thus subject to factors for which no suitable correction can be introduced.

On the whole the women have increased in the same ratio as the men, but to a less marked degree. A further confirmation of this statement is found upon comparison of indices which on account of lack of material are limited to three.

TABLE 145

COMPARISON OF INDICES OF MALE AND FEMALE STUDENTS BY GENERATION

	35 Years Ago			Today		
	Male	Female	Difference	Male	Female	Difference
Relative sitting height	52.30	52.59	.29	51.91	52.74	.83
Relative girth of chest (N)	49.93	46.81	−3.12	51.20	47.41	−3.79
Relative girth of waist	41.89	38.12	−3.77	41.40	39.60	−1.80

The increased relative sitting height shows an accentuation of the feminine tendency towards a proportionally longer trunk length. There is a drop in relative girth of chest (N) showing that in relation to height there was less increase among women than among men.

In general, changes which have occurred are the same in both males and females. In both sexes the pelvic measurements and shoulder measurements have altered in the same way and vary only in degree. The pelvic breadth has decreased during the space of one generation, but the girth measurements have increased, indicating an addition of adipose tissue, a fleshy rather than a skeletal increase.

The change cannot indicate any special advance from an evolutionary point of view, inasmuch as the more advanced pelves, at least in the male, are broader and shallower. Physically also the change is probably not for the better, since the decreased pelvic breadth in the females cannot be considered as a good sign from the point of view of child-bearing.

In shoulder measurements, although there has been an increase in breadth in both sexes, this increase has been at the sacrifice of depth, for the chest expansion in both instances has decreased.

In the women the increase in waist measurements is definitely a valuable one, for it indicates a substantial improvement in bodily proportions.

In stature, where the most marked increases have taken place, the proportional increases in both male and female have been practically equal. During the past eighty years there has been a mean increment per annum of .08 centimeters, or one centimeter every twelve and one-half years, and statistically considered the mean period for a significant difference to manifest itself is about eight and one-half years. The rate of increase has not been regular. It reached its highest peak in those born during the decade 1866–75, immediately prior to which there was only a slight rise, and subsequent to which a gradual decline to the present rate of about .06–.07 centimeters took place. We can only surmise that, were the decline in annual increment to continue at its present rate, the student population at least would reach a position of equilibrium during the next forty or fifty years. This figure is purely conjectural, and fails to take into consideration numerous elements, both favorable and unfavorable, which in their several ways may profoundly change the ultimate results.

The accompanying table illustrates the increases per decade as distinguished sexually:

TABLE 146

INCREASES IN STATURE FOR MALES AND FEMALES BY BIRTH DECADES

	1836–45	1846–55	1856–65	1866–75	1876–85	1886–95	1896–05	M
Male	.08	−.04	.15	.12	.07	.10	.07	.08
Female	...	...	−.02	.12	.15	.07	.10	.08

The slight differences are probably to be accounted for on the basis of numerical inferiority of the females, although the means for the two groups are identical. Complementary to the increase in stature has been an increase in weight, which likewise shows considerable uniformity in both sexes.

In conclusion it should be stated that such changes as have occurred in the student population at large during the past generation at least, and in all probability over a longer period, have shown little sexual difference. Both male and female students exhibit the same tendencies, the causes and nature of which are briefly summarized in the conclusive remarks.

CAUSES OF INCREASE IN STATURE

In the following attempt to explain the various causes of the phenomenon of stature increase, no attention is paid to the undoubtedly large field which in its broader definition might be called psychic effect. Only the factors of race and what in its inclusive sense is termed environment are taken into consideration.

By environment is understood firstly geographical location — continental, latitudinal, altitudinal, meteorological, and climatological; secondly local setting, urban or rural; thirdly immediate surroundings — social conditions, home occupation; and lastly physical conditions — food, clothing, medical attention, sleep, amount of exercise, etcetera. All the categories doubtless have some part in the transformation, and together with race are discussed in sequence.

It may be that change of geographical environment has its effect upon stature. For this continent Boas [1] has shown that in the case of immigrants with widely divergent characteristics there is a tendency to approach the norm of the general population in the second generation. An example is the comparison of Norwegians in Norway with the figures given by Baxter, which show how very materially changed environment has influenced stature. Schreiner [2] concludes that the difference is due not wholly to age but also to the increase in bodily development resulting from better living conditions. Changes in altitude and latitude may have some effect on the increase in stature, as well as change of occupation and moving from rural into urban districts. It has frequently been shown that city dwellers are taller than those in rural districts, although it may be that urban life attracts the taller people. We cannot be sure that cities produce taller people. Occupation likewise may be a contributory factor, but here again the difference may be due to selection rather than to a tendency towards change. Probably more important than any of the considerations thus far advanced is the matter of physical conditions: increased medical attention, abundance of food, greater care of the body, more appropriate exercise, more attention to the numerous details of sanitation and improved hygienic conditions, increased prosperity, and the multiplication of luxuries.

[1] *Changes in Bodily Form of Descendants of Immigrants*, Immigration Commission Report, Washington (1911).
[2] Bryn and Schreiner (1929), p. 25.

The various elements which have engaged our attention might be included, for want of a better word, in the term "modernization." This connotes a kind of speeding up process, a stimulative force which is likewise sympathetic with the causative factors enumerated above. Concerning this rather comprehensive and embracing set of factors, let us turn to its relationship to race. We have seen that increase is not limited to Europe alone, but includes certain Asiatic peoples as well. Data of sufficient accuracy cannot be had for the remainder of the Eurasiatic Continent, nor for Africa and South America. For these larger areas we must await more detailed measurements by which the increase, if any, may be determined. All of the instances cited have been from areas where western culture and civilization either are indigenous or, as in the case of Japan, have been adopted wholesale. The question remains, had Japan not become westernized would stature have remained constant? In other words, has the civilizing process in its modern sense a direct bearing on the living conditions to such an extent that stature is distinctly modified? If such a premise were assumed, it would be logical to expect the greatest increment in areas of highest cultural contact and centralization. We should expect it in the Euramerican and Japanese areas.

As a corollary it would follow that in regions of least change culturally the greatest uniformity or persistence of stature would obtain. We should expect that in Africa, the greater parts of Asia, and practically all of the insular areas, little if any change would have taken place unless from race mixture or uncontrollable external forces.

We have observed that the Mediterraneans fall lowest in rate of increase, with the Alpines highest and the Nordics intermediate. Are we therefore justified in concluding that there is consequently racial segregation also; or are we to assume, on the other hand, some accidental relationship? In either case the fact of the increase remains.

Further there is the question of morphological type. Both the Mediterraneans and the Nordics are long-headed, whereas the Alpines and the Japanese are broad-headed. May there not be some connection, therefore, between morphological type and intensity of stature increase? We can hardly determine the relative degrees of increase until we have more information; the various racial differences noted above may not be correct, and we must wait till future data have fixed their proper positions. It is quite conceivable also that, whereas the above order might be true today, the reverse might hold within a few decades, for it has already been shown that increase is extremely variable, and is susceptible of change by numerous factors.

Leaving the question of priority unsettled until further information is available for confirmation or denial of the respective racial positions, let us examine the causes which more nearly concern us at present, i. e. the immediate reasons for stature change in Old American students.

We have here a population which has remained racially the same over a considerable period, homogeneous in language and in inherited cultural background, and in the data used in the present study equivalent in age. The number of factors in the solution of the problem is therefore considerably reduced. We have seen that the occupations of the fathers of the present generation have changed slightly, the category of manual workers having slightly decreased. Since manual workers tend to run lower in stature than professional men and urban dwellers (the workers were largely farmers), a slight but negligible increase might thereby be accounted for.

The proportions of oldest to younger brothers can have little bearing, for although we have seen that with successive juniority there is increase both in stature and in weight, families are getting smaller. Hence, even were we to assume that with increase in the number of children up to a given point (to the limit of greatest parental fecundity) stature would increase, since families are getting smaller, this explanation helps us not at all.

Such factors as assortive and selective mating may have their place, but their significance in the present work cannot be determined, since measurements are lacking for the mothers. Hooton offers as one of the primary causes the various improvements in medical care and hygienic attention which have come within the past hundred years. In most families, he holds, there is born a certain percentage of children who outgrow their strength before they have reached adolescence and maturity. These children are more subject to diseases than those who grow in proportion to their physical and resistive strength. Generally these children are the younger ones, and therefore, according to conclusions reached above, should be taller. He suggests that improved methods of medical attention tide over these children who by the law of survival of the fittest should normally have died.

Accepting this hypothesis, it would appear that by artificial aid we are helping to increase our mean stature by alleviating the struggle for existence for those who have outgrown their strength, until they have been able to adjust themselves by equalizing strength with body size, and thus have become more thoroughly immunized against disease. Further, since nature demands some compensation for any favors given, there must be some weaknesses resultant from what appears on the surface to be a most remarkable accomplishment and an apparent victory over the forces of nature.

We have already noted that, despite the advantage of increased stature and weight, these increases are offset to a degree by the decrease in chest expansion and the decrease, especially in the female, of pelvic breadth. It may be also that the increased proportion of heart diseases in the past few decades is partly caused by the taxing of the heart muscles in earlier life.

Whatever the results, either in increase of stature and weight or in other measurements, the offsetting harmful effects probably balance the scales, and it is very doubtful whether the changes which on the surface appear so beneficial are really good, since a more careful study has revealed factors decidedly detrimental.

In conclusion we may briefly summarize the causes for increase in stature in the student group of Old Americans in probable order of importance:

(1) Increased medical attention in preserving those children who have outgrown their strength until they have reached maturity and a normal state of resistance to disease.

(2) Cultural modernization and a general speeding up process.

(3) Better food in more abundance and in greater variety.

(4) More exercise.

(5) Possible assortive and selective mating on the part of parents.

(6) Occupational change of parents.

(7) The non-ascertainable element of climatological and meteorological effect.

Bibliography

BAXTER, J. H.
  Statistics, Medical and Anthropological, of the Provost-Marshal General's Bureau,
  vol. I (1875)

BOAS, F.
  The Growth of First-born Children, Science, N. S., vol. I, no. 15 (1895)
  Changes in Bodily Form of Descendants of Immigrants, Immigration Commis-
  sion Report, Washington (1911)

BRYN, H., AND SCHREINER, K. E.
  Somatologie der Norweger (1929)

CASTLE, W. E.
  Genetics and Eugenics (1926)

HITCHCOCK, E., AND SEELYE, H. H.
  Statistics Bearing upon the Average and Typical Student in Amherst College,
  Journal Anthropological Institute, vols. XVII and XVIII (1888)

HRDLIČKA, A.
  Old Americans (1925)

HULSE, F.
  Unpublished Data, Peabody Museum, Cambridge, Massachusetts (1930)

JACKSON, C. M.
  Measurements of Female Students of the University of Minnesota, American
  Journal Physical Anthropology, vol. XIV (1930)

LIVI, R.
  Anthropometria Militare (1896)

LOMBROSO, C.
  Sulla Statura degli Italiani, Archivo per l'Antropologia e la Etnologia, vol. III
  (1873)

LUNDBORG, H., AND LINDERS, F. J.
  Racial Characters of the Swedish Nation (1926)

LUTZ, F. E.
  Note on the Influence of Change in Sex on the Intensity of Heredity, Biometrika,
  vol. II (1903)

MARTIN, R.
  Lehrbuch der Anthropologie, 2nd edition (1928)

MATSUMURA, A.
  On the Cephalic Index and Stature of the Japanese and Their Local Differences,
  Journal Faculty of Science, Imperial University of Tokyo, Section V, Anthro-
  pology, vol. I (1925)

OLORIZ, D. F.
  Discursos Leidos en la Real Academia de Medicina (1896)

PEARSON, K., AND LEE, A.
  On the Laws of Inheritance in Man, Biometrika, vol. II (1903)

POWYS, A. O.
  Data for the Problem of Evolution in Man, Biometrika, vol. I (1901)

RETZIUS, G., AND FURST, C. M.
  Anthropoligica Suecica (1902)
  Rolls of the Soldiers of the Revolutionary War, New Hampshire State Papers,
    vol. II, Concord, New Hampshire
SARGENT, D. A.
  The Physique of Scholars, Athletes, and the Average Student, Popular Science
    Monthly, vol. LXXIII (1908)
WISSLER, C.
  Relation of Nature to Man in Aboriginal North America (1926)
YOSHIDA, Y.
  On the Development of Stature, Weight, and Head Circumference of the Japanese,
    Journal Anthropological Society, Tokyo, vol. XLIII, no. 484 (1928)